Potters

Edited by Emmanuel Cooper and Eileen Lewenstein

An illustrated directory of the work of Fellows and Professional Members of the Craft Potters Association of Great Britain

A guide to visiting potters in their workshops

A source for studying pottery in the United Kingdom

Ninth Edition

Individual entries in the directory have been supplied
by the members concerned.

Edited by Emmanuel Cooper and Eileen Lewenstein
assisted by Daphne Matthews and Marilyn Kopkin.

Cover - Derek Emms, glaze detail

Photographs supplied by individual potters or from Ceramic Review

Book design by Ceramic Review

Potters

First Edition	1972
Second Edition	1974
Third Edition	1975
Fourth Edition	1977
Fifth Edition	1980
Sixth Edition	1983
Seventh Edition	1986
Eighth Edition	1989
Ninth Edition	1992

ISBN 0 9504767 8 1

Published by Ceramic Review Publishing Ltd.
21 Carnaby Street, London W1V 1PH
© Ceramic Review Publishing Ltd 1992
Typeset and Printed by Bushey Mead Press Ltd., Hailsham, England

Potters

Ninth Edition

Contents

Introduction

'Potters' the illustrated directory of the work of Fellows and Professional Members of the Craft Potters Association has proved to be a useful guide to pots and potters in the United Kingdom. This, the ninth edition has been completely revised. Illustrations of potters at work reflect the current interest in the maker as well as the object and set the scene, placing the pot in its studio context.

The first section, the directory, between pages 9-246, illustrates the work made by Fellows and Professional Members of the Craft Potters Association, listed in their alphabetical orders. It shows potters and their pots, together with a brief description of the type of work they make. Biographical notes are supplied by the potters themselves, and photographs illustrate recent work. Workshop and individual potters marks are included as an aid to identification. The directory gives a good indication of work that is being made today. It shows the range and diversity of contemporary ceramics, and it also serves as a useful record for future reference.

In the section 'Visiting A Potter' (Pages 247-268), names, addresses and telephone numbers of members of the Craft Potters Association of Great Britain are listed together with details of visiting times, showroom opening and so on — invaluable information for anyone planning a visit. Some potters welcome callers to their showrooms and studios and some allow visitors to their showrooms only. This information is clearly stated together with the opening hours. Many of the potters have indicated that they welcome visitors, but by appointment only. If you wish to visit a potter who can only see you by appointment please write or telephone beforehand. A specially drawn map shows where workshops and studios open to the public are situated. 'Becoming a Potter' is a valuable guide to a wide range of learning opportunities. It lists degree and vocational courses available at art schools, colleges and institutions of higher education and has been completely revised for this edition. It also contains information on part-time study. There is also useful advice on how to apply to work with potters in their workshops.

The Craft Potters Association is the largest organisation of studio potters in Britain and has 158 Fellows and 82 Professional Members. We are sure that this new edition will prove as useful a guide to contemporary ceramics in the United Kingdom as the previous one. Every effort has been made to ensure that the information included is correct at the time of printing.

The Craft Potters Association

The Association was formed as the Craftsmen Potters Association in 1958 as a co-operative to sell the work of its potter members and to increase general awareness of the craft. In 1955 purchase tax was extended to include domestic ware. This led Walter Lipton who was then at the Rural Industries Bureau, in a move to help potters, to arrange an exhibition of pottery for export; it was bought complete by a New Zealand store. This success prompted a group of potters to appoint a working party to consider ways and means of forming an association that could organise similar activities.

Under the guidance of Walter Lipton the Craftsmen Potters Association was formed as an Industrial and Provident Society — Rosemary Wren was elected the first chairman and David Canter was appointed Honorary Secretary. The organisation is democratic; upon election each Fellow and Professional Member buys a £1 share and is entitled to elect Council Members and to vote at the Annual General Meeting. Policy decisions are made at Council Meetings when ideas from members are discussed.

The CPA faces the nineties with over thirty years experience behind it, and with confidence in the future of the craft. Recent changes in the administration and structure of the association have brought it more in line with current practice. The new category of Professional Member has extended and opened up the number of potters who can take part in this remarkable organisation, while the wide and inventive activities of the Associates have taken membership to an impressive 700. The establishment of The Craft Pottery Charitable Trust to further the educational aspects of the Association is a recognition of the importance of this work and the continuing need to educate and interest the public in the craft and to make information available to all potters. Equally useful has been the setting up of the two trading companies, one dealing with the retail activities of Contemporary Ceramics, the other with Ceramic Review Publishing. All is under the watchful eye of the elected Council of the Craft Potters Association, the potters who give their time and energy to maintaining the democratic and fair basis on which the CPA was founded — a noble intent whereby the CPA continues to be owned and controlled by its elected members.

Contemporary Ceramics

The Council decided early on to open a shop, known as the Craftsmen Potters Shop, to sell the work of its members in the heart of London's West End. In the Spring of 1959 a lease was taken on premises in Lowndes Court, Carnaby Street before the street gained its present fame. The interior of the shop and basement was built by a team of volunteers who worked in their free time for the following twelve months. On May 30th 1960 the shop opened with a superb exhibition of Ray Finch's stoneware.

In March 1966 the Association acquired larger shop premises in a building being erected in Marshall Street on the site of the house where William Blake was born. David Attenborough performed the opening ceremony of the new shop on December 4th 1967.

In 1988 the rear part of the shop was converted into the David Canter Gallery to commemorate the work and achievement of the Association's first Honorary Secretary. Major exhibitions by established members of the CPA and shows by potters at the start of their career are held in it. The gallery also contains a 'Collector's Cabinet' of work by early studio potters such as Bernard Leach, Michael Cardew, Katharine Pleydell-Bouverie and Denise Wren, all one-time members of the CPA, whose work is now finding a new and appreciative audience. 'Contemporary Ceramics' is unique in Central

London selling and exhibiting only studio pots. The shop also has a well equipped sundries section which stocks sponges, cones, turning tools, cane handles, Japanese brushes, sieves etc. all at very competitive prices. A good range of magazines on pottery are on sale as well as postcards of specially photographed pots. Fellows, Professional, Associate and Junior Members are entitled to a 10% discount on all purchases except books.

In 1990 the shop adopted the new name Contemporary Ceramics, the Craft Potters Shop and Gallery. Improvements to the interior display continue to be made, the latest being an enlarged Books section showing a large selection of current titles — an excellent place to browse and make new discoveries.

Association Membership

The CPA is the only national body representing potters. Fellows are elected by the Council and are entitled to vote at A.G.Ms and to show work in 'Contemporary Ceramics'. Professional Members are also elected by the Council and are also able to vote at A.G.Ms. They may be invited to show their work in 'Contemporary Ceramics' from time to time or in special exhibitions. Associate membership is open to anyone interested in ceramics.

Association Activities

As well as 158 Fellows and 82 Professional members, the Craft Potters Association has an average of 600 associate members who contribute much to its activites. Many of the association's activities are the responsibility of council sub-committees. CPA Archives are under the care of Moira Vincentelli at Aberystwyth Arts Centre (University College of Wales). Evening meetings have included talks by eminent potters from both this country and overseas. Recent talks have been given by David Leach who demonstrated his unique working methods. Weekend events are arranged from time to time, the most recent of which was the two-day Festival of European Ceramics, in July 1992. Publication has also started of a regular newsletter for all members 'CPA News'. This carries news of shop and association activities, a lively letters section plus articles by members. Associate Members receive advance information of such events, priority booking, reduced fees and invitations to private views of exhibitions.

Ceramic Review Publications

The internationally acclaimed magazine 'Ceramic Review' a contemporary survey of studio pottery, is now published by the newly formed subsidiary company Ceramic Review Publications Ltd. It appears six times a year and has a wide circulation both in this country and abroad. Members can subscribe to the magazine at a reduced rate. Other publications are 'The Ceramic Review Book of Clay Bodies and Glaze Recipes' (4th edition 1988) which includes over 700 recipes from professional potters and has much useful advice on mixing and using bodies and glazes. 'Potters Tips' edited by Robert Fournier, brought together the many useful tips published in Ceramic Review over the last 20 years and was published in 1990.

Illustrated Directory of CPA Fellows

Most Fellows of the Association have work on sale at Contemporary Ceramics the Craft Potters Shop. A full list of Fellows together with their addresses, can be found on page 248.

Lead Release

The Craft Potters Association is fully aware of the possible danger to health of cadmium or lead released from glazed pottery into food. The CPA council requires all members sending work to the shop to state whether lead or cadmium are used in their pottery or not. If these materials are present then potters must have their work tested regularly and produce certificates to show that it conforms to the new British Standard BS6748. The public can buy safely from the CPA shop.

Adrian Abberley

Adrian Abberley works alone making individual pieces and some domestic ware in oxidised stoneware and porcelain, using a combination of slab built and thrown sections.

Tim Andrews

Tim Andrews Born Torquay Devon. Trained with David Leach 1978-79 and at Dartington Pottery training workshop 1979-81. Received Crafts Council setting up grant 1981 and started own studio in Exeter. Moved to second workshop in '83 making mostly domestic stoneware and porcelain and running a series of international summer workshops. In 1986 returned to Lowerdown Pottery to share studio with David Leach. About five years ago decided to move away from decorated stoneware and porcelain (although he still makes limited quantities of both) to concentrate more on form and surface quality. Uses Raku and smoking techniques with burnishing and some enamels. 'My pots are hybrids of different clays, slips, colours and glazes fired to an assortment of temperatures'

Mick Arnup

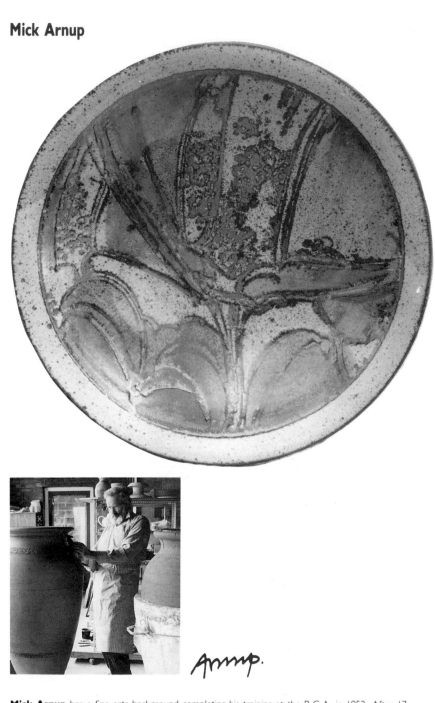

Arnup.

Mick Arnup has a fine arts background completing his training at the R.C.A. in 1953. After 17 years at York School of Art he left teaching and built new workshops, a 70 cu.ft. oil-fired kiln and a showroom at Holtby near York. Since 1972 he has been a full time potter making a range of reduced decorated stoneware, architectural ceramics, numerals and letters. He is presently making seriously large pots using moulds and the Cretan slow wheel. Exhibits regularly in U.K. and abroad, often with his wife Sally Arnup, the animal sculptor.

Keith Ashley

Keith Ashley Born Yeovil, Somerset 1944. Trained at Farnham Art College 1962-65. Studio at Highgate Pottery, London. Produces thrown domestic stoneware and large, handbuilt individual forms. Lively, honest, unpretentious, substantial, simple yet complicated are some of the qualities Keith Ashley strives to give to his pots. He believes that good pots serve not only as prospective containers but are themselves already containers of something of the essence of the potter that made them. He draws on the sophisticated skills acquired as a student of both Dan Arbeid and Gwyn Hanssen and seeks to combine them with the unselfconscious expression he so admires in his mature, untrained students.

Chris Aston

Chris Aston — established full-time potter for 25 years, has workshops and showroom adjoining his 18th century cottage at Elkesley, North Nottinghamshire. Since he first went full-time in 1967, Chris's work has reflected the many changes and fluctuations in the pottery world. From the rustic colourings and very matt finishes sought by early customers, Chris's later work has become more sophisticated and individual and, with the development of a unique copper-based decorative technique giving a glowing berry-like patterning on both domestic and exhibition pots, is constantly recognisable to collectors throughout the country. His current work is moving further from the domestic, with lustres giving jewel-like finishes to slender bottles and bowls. As well as the decorative aspects of pottery, Chris also enjoys the more scientific and technical problems which confront every potter, and works continually to maintain and improve the quality of his glazes and clay bodies, using chemical analyses and molecular formulae. He gives particular attention to the preparation of his own clay blend of fine ball clay, china clay, feldspar and quartz, using a blunger for mixing and filter press for drying the slip, and finally vacuum pugging of the clay. Liquid ligno-sulphate is added to the blend at the slip stage, and this material, often used in the heavy clay industry as a clay conditioner and particle lubricant, gives remarkable extra plasticity and workability as well as very even drying. The resulting clay when fired is tough, durable and chip resistant.
The glazed pots are fired in a 90 cu.ft. reduction oil-fired kiln, and lustres are fired in self-built electric kilns.

Felicity Aylieff

F. AYLIEFF.

Felicity Aylieff has a degree in Ceramics from Bath Academy of Art (1976) and is presently a lecturer at Bath College of Higher Education and visiting lecturer at Goldsmiths' College, London. Her pieces are handbuilt using a white earthenware clay. The decorating and/or building technique used on the pots could loosely be described as agateware, with some forms being coiled up in a variety of bodystained clays, and others made of a single colour and finally inlaid with mixed coloured clay (agate) shapes. Glaze is rarely used, the pieces being fired to 1220°C to vitrify the clay. Forms have evolved through the re-examination of familiar proportion, and the interplay and relationship of decoration to form. Ceramic solutions often rely on a visual drama, illusion or similar theatre, with colour being of fundamental importance. She has exhibited widely throughout Britain and abroad.

Svend Bayer

Svend Bayer makes woodfired stoneware garden pots and domestic pots. These are influenced by rural France, provincial Chinese and early American stoneware, and are fired in a large woodfired, crossdraught, single chamber kiln of some 800 cu.ft. Mostly the pots rely on fly ash, although the insides of all the domestic pots are glazed and all the bowls, plates and dishes are glazed and decorated.

Michael Bayley

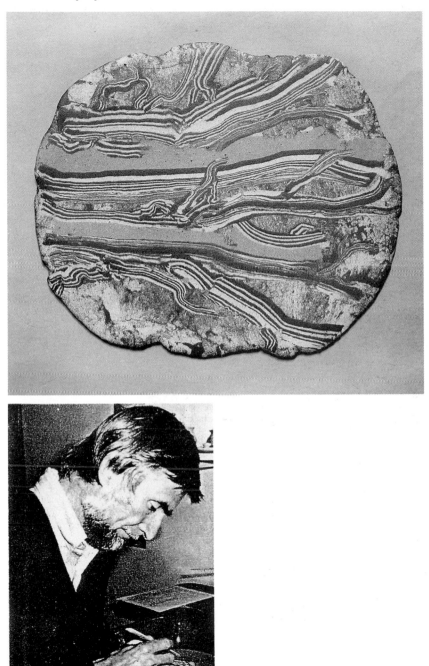

Michael Bayley trained at Hornsey College of Art in the 1950s. Individual handbuilt ceramics, including dishes and wall pieces. Oxidised stoneware, mostly unglazed. Inlaid decoration.

Peter Beard

PFB

Peter Beard makes thrown and handbuilt individual pieces in stoneware and porcelain with glazes built up in multiple layers using wax as a resist between the layers to create patterns. High and low temperature glazes with coloured pigments are used to achieve matt and fluid textures giving a wide range of pastel to strong colours. Exhibits in one man and mixed exhibitions in many countries and has work in private and public collections. Regularly gives demonstrations and slide lectures in Europe, Australia and New Zealand. Part-time lecturer at the Kent Institute of Art and Design. Council member of the CPA. Awarded various grants and scholarships for study and travel.

Beverley Bell-Hughes

Beverley Bell-Hughes. Born Epsom 1948. Trained at Sutton School of Art 1965-67. Harrow Studio Pottery Course 1967-69 under Victor Margrie and Michael Casson. Work has been exhibited abroad and at home. 'My work is handbuilt and the shapes governed by both the making process and my interest in natural growth. My aim is to get across the feeling of the material clay, creating a bond with natural forms, whilst at the same time preserving the identity of the pot by it being a usable container if need be. I do not set out to imitate nature, but aspire to echo the process of nature'.

Terry Bell-Hughes

Terry Bell-Hughes trained at Harrow School of Art 1967 under Victor Margrie and Michael Casson. Primarily interested in high-fired domestic pots thrown in series reflecting influences from Oriental and British country pots. Exhibited in several 'one person' and many shared exhibitions in Britain and abroad. Work included in several public and private collections.

Maggie Angus Berkowitz

Maggie Angus Berkowitz makes wall and floor panels of glazed tile. Work is usually commissioned, often figurative, and always individually designed for a specific site; she enjoys discussing projects with clients. Past installations include floors for schools, with games, visual puns, heraldic signs; sundials; commemorative tiles; illustrative panels for offices, hospital and leisure centre. Many domestic designs for garden, kitchen and bathroom. Uses earthenware glazes on industrial blanks, quarries and ironstone tiles. Trained, taught and worked in U.K., Italy, Tanzania, U.S.A. and Japan. Exhibits occasionally.

Clive Bowen

Clive Bowen The pottery was established in 1971. The pots are thrown in red earthenware clay and range from large scale store jars and garden pots to mugs and egg cups. The domestic ware and one-off pots may be decorated with three contrasting slips using slip trailing, combing and sgraffito methods. His pots are once-fired in a round (8′dia) down-draught woodfired kiln to 1040°C-1060°C (less for garden pots).

Loretta Braganza

Braganza (signature)

Loretta Braganza trained in Graphics with a fine arts background. Painting illusory space on a tightly sculptured form is a continuing pre-occupation. Shapes are archetypal and are mainly influenced by childhood spent in India. The decorative slipware is a constantly evolving technique using a combination of coloured slips and underglaze colours. Works chiefly for exhibitions and commissions.

Carlo Briscoe and Edward Dunn

Carlo Briscoe and Edward Dunn, two Fine Art graduates, took up ceramics eight years ago. 'We have been working full-time under the trading name of 'Reptile' since 1988. We have combined on many projects, both large and small, and produce flat and relief tin-glazed tiles and wall plaques. Our influences are many and varied, but include Persian and Early European ceramics. We sell to shops and galleries all over the U.K. and in the U.S.A. We also work to commission and have completed various projects for kitchens, bathrooms and swimming-pool surrounds in this country and abroad.'

Sandy Brown

Sandy Brown trained in Japan. Widely exhibited in U.K., Japan, U.S.A., Australia and Europe. Runs workshops on Intuition and Creativity; lectures and demonstrates worldwide. Work consists of: Inner Journey; Clay Sculptures. A personal therapeutic narrative from Flying Figures to Goddesses to Lovers. Outer Journey: Pots for Food. Expressive lively pots showing the tactile sensuality of clay with fresh spontaneous decoration.

Ian Byers

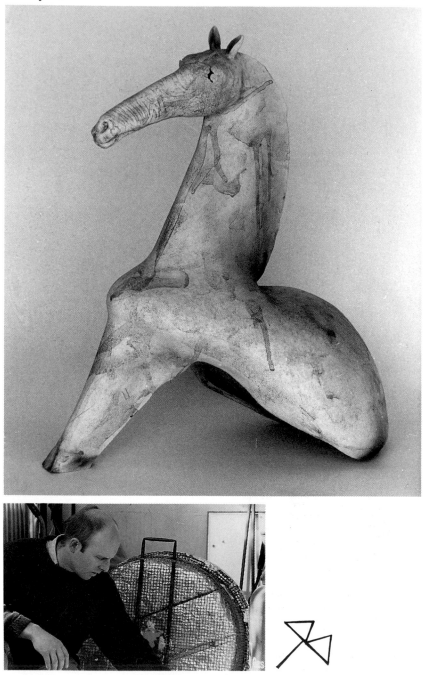

Ian Byers 'The preoccupations of my work are both poetic and sculptural, often drawing together ideas and images to create a mood and interplay. Most of the work is low fired and Raku smoked'. Ian Byers is the author of *Raku* part of 'The Complete Potter' series published by Batsford, and has work in collections in Britain and Europe.

Alan Caiger-Smith

Alan Caiger-Smith

Edgar Campden

Alan Caiger-Smith at Aldermaston Pottery (founded 1955) works in tin-glaze earthenware and reduction-lustre, assisted for the last thirty years by Edgar Campden, for thirteen years by Julian Bellmont, and for eight years by Andrew Hazelden, and at present also by Louise Bashall and Silke Nerger. The output ranges from tableware and tiles to ceremonial pieces and commissions, wheel-thrown, handbuilt, jolleyed, or modelled in relief. The work often has strong calligraphic painting, imagery or inscriptions, and recently some very large pots have been made, three and four feet high, with lustre designs. Most of the pots are wood-fired with off-cuts from cricket-bat willows. Work is included in many public and private collections in the U.K. and overseas and exhibitions have been held in the U.S.A and Canada, Australia and New Zealand, Japan, the Netherlands, Sweden and Spain and in the U.K. Author of *Tin-Glaze Pottery* (Faber 1973), *Lustre Pottery* (Faber 1985 and The Herbert Press 1991 in paperback), and editor with Ronald Lightbown of *Piccolpasso's Three Books of the Potter's Art* (Scolar Press 1980). M.B.E. 1988.

John Calver

John Calver I was twenty two when captivated by my first contact with clay. Four years later I gave up my civil engineering career to pot full time. Initially I made domestic earthenware but, seduced by high temperature glazes, I changed to reduced stoneware. My forms are all thrown on the wheel and remain functional but have become progressively more highly decorated. The surface may be textured with fabric, clay stamps, rope or chattering; slips are brushed, sponged, trailed or inlaid; and finally, after biscuit firing, up to seven glazes are poured in partly overlapping layers.'

Seth Cardew

Seth Cardew. The idea that the Wenford Bridge Pottery stands for is that tradition is outward-looking and face to face with living people. On the subject of tradition, Michael Cardew, the world famous stylist who founded the Wenford Bridge Pottery in 1939, would quote William Blake's little known but profound words: 'Eternity is in love with the productions of Time'. The second and third generations at Wenford Bridge Pottery continue to uphold this idea and produce hand made, hand decorated, wood-fired stoneware.

Daphne Carnegy

Daphne Carnegy trained in various workshops in France and at Harrow School of Art. Set up own studio at Kingsgate Workshops in 1980 and since then has been producing a range of colourful tin-glazed domestic ware. All pieces are thrown in red earthenware and after the bisque firing, are painted in the maiolica technique on the unfired glaze, using oxides and underglaze colours, decoration being mainly derived from fruit and floral designs. Sells through shops and galleries throughout the U.K. and abroad.

Michael Casson

Michael Casson Early member of CPA 1957/58. Chairman early 1960s. Council member until early 1970s. Co-founder of Harrow studio-pottery course 1963 (with Victor Margrie), Founder board member of Dartington Pottery Training workshop; 1983 OBE, 1985-88 Vice-Chairman of Crafts Council. Books: *Pottery in Britain Today*, 1966, *Craft of the Potter* 1976 (Presenter of BBC TV series). First pots 1945. First workshop London 1952-59. Tin-glazed earthenware. Second workshop 1959-77 Buckinghamshire, full range of domestic stoneware with Sheila Casson. Present workshop wood and gas fired saltglaze, individual functional pots, jugs, jars etc, most recently figuratively decorated bowls 'swimmers'.

Sheila Casson

Sheila Casson 1955 shared workshop with Michael Casson in London making tin-glazed earthenware fired in an electric kiln. Early member of CPA 1958. 1959 domestic stoneware oxidised in an electric kiln, subsequently reduction fired in a gas kiln. 1977 moved to present workshop making individual pieces in stoneware and porcelain with decoration inspired by the Herefordshire landscape. The technique is a combination of sprayed slips with paper resist and sgraffito, biscuit fired and then glazed in a reduction gas kiln at 1280°C. Recently my decoration has gone more abstract. Since 1990 I am also making saltglaze jugs, teapots and vases.

Jenny Clarke

Jenny Clarke trained at Farnham School of Art in the 1960s under Paul Barron and Henry Hammond. Shared a workshop with Sally Dawson, in London, for several years; during this time spent one summer working for David Leach. After a year in New Zealand in 1971, travelling and contacting different craftspeople, returned to England and shared a studio with Ian Godfrey. Moved to Bristol in 1974, where home and workshop are now combined. Produces a wide range of domestic stoneware, using slips and sgraffito decoration. Also producing a range of porcelain work, using spraying techniques for decoration. Sells and exhibits at a number of craft galleries.

Derek Clarkson

Derek Clarkson has been engaged in ceramics for over forty years, lecturing; demonstrating; exhibiting; and full time potting since 1980. Works alone making porcelain and stoneware bottles and bowls by throwing and turning. Firing - 1300°C. with reducing atmosphere. Waxy ash glazes with cobalt and iron brush decoration predominate. Celadon, tenmoku, kaki, titanium and copper red glazes also used. Burnishing gold is frequently added. Porcelain bowls are translucent, often with fine incised designs exploring graduations of translucency. Recent work includes somewhat capricious zinc silica crystalline porcelain. Represented in many private collections and public galleries including the Victoria and Albert Museum.

Margery Clinton

Margery Clinton Diploma in Drawing and Painting, Glasgow School of Art, MA Royal College of Art, School of Ceramics. I work with one associate, Evelyn Corbett. Together we make a collection of tiles and lamps and pots. Mostly these are in stoneware or porcelain glazed with feldspathic glazes and further decoration and firing with in-glaze reduction lustre glazes. The tiles and a few pots are earthenware using the in-glaze reduction method or the traditional clay-paste Hispano Moresque one. The illustration shows a large one off tile. Developing reduction lustre glaze colours and effects has continued to dominate my work since beginning research at the Royal College of Art in 1973. My book *Lustres* published by Batsford in 1991 gives details of methods. We also offer a few summer workshops at the pottery here in Haddington.

Pieces are either signed or painted with a mark. Collections include HRH The Duke of Edinburgh Victoria and Albert Museum, Tate Gallery, Royal Museum of Scotland, Glasgow Museum and Art Gallery.

Peter Clough

Peter Clough 'I trained at Portsmouth College of Art, and Manchester University, and have been potting both full and part-time for over twenty years. My current work is thrown, altered and assembled, then fired in saggars with sawdust or salt, but all making and firing processes are variable, and depend upon the ideas being explored. My principal concerns at this time are with the vessel as object, and with function and content in a wide context. I have recently begun to explore clay in conjunction with metals, notably bronze, silver, and cast iron. Actively involved with the Northern Potters Association. Senior Lecturer at the University College of Ripon and York St. John, - (Ripon Campus).'

Russell Coates

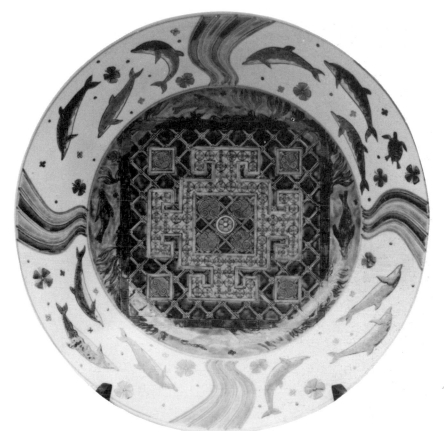

Russell Coates Since moving out of London to the West Country, my work has changed. I now combine dolphins, sea creatures and a variety of birds with patterns which are derived from Celtic and Old English designs. I still use the traditional old Kutani colours — red, yellow, green, blue and purple on porcelain. To begin with the bones of the design are marked out with underglaze blue on the biscuit ware. After the 1270°C reduction glaze firing the bright glassy enamels are painted on and fired to 840°C. If gold is employed in the design it is also included in the enamel firing and burnished afterwards with agate. I aim to achieve a jewel like quality with the enamels in intricate patterns in the centres or in borders.

Roger Cockram

Roger Cockram Born in North Devon. Originally trained as a scientist (B.Sc.Hons. Zoology, London). Post-graduate research in marine ecology. Accepted for Harrow course 1973-75. Since 1976 has run own studio making mainly large wood-fired thrown ware. Moved to current premises in 1986. Recent work mainly individual pieces based on marine and freshwater themes, sometimes with added modelling and referring to animals in their own surroundings. All work once-fired to cone 10 in a small gas kiln. Work sells through own showroom, galleries in U.K., U.S.A., Germany, France and Switzerland; also through exhibitions and commission.

Russell Collins

Russell Collins A small team of potters produce work mostly for the catering market. It is all reduction fired in two 110 cu.ft. gas kilns. Clients include all the major hotel and restaurant chains on a worldwide basis. A smaller range of domestic ware is also produced as well as individual pieces for commission. The complete ranges can be seen in the showroom at the pottery.

Barbara Colls

Barbara Colls attended part time pottery classes over many years at West Surrey College of Art and Design, initially under Henry Hammond, Paul Barron and his wife Penny who were all a great help in developing the bird lidded pots. Now works alone in tiny studio, mainly in oxidised stoneware and porcelain using coloured slips and glazes. Exhibitions at Guildford House, Black Horse Craft Centre Norwich and at many galleries at home and abroad.

Joanna Constantinidis

Joanna Constantinidis Individual pots in stoneware and porcelain, also some porcelain tableware.

Delan Cookson

Delan Cookson 'I make individual thrown bottles, bowls or container forms in porcelain and am chiefly concerned with exploring thrown and turned forms, discovering endless variations on my chosen themes. Many are achieved by joining more than one section as in the example above. I like porcelain because its smooth whiteness reflects all the brilliance of my coloured glazes. I enjoy working on my own and have been potting full time since 1989 after twenty eight years of lecturing in ceramics. Work has been shown widely particularly in the South West and is in many public and private collections.

Bennett Cooper

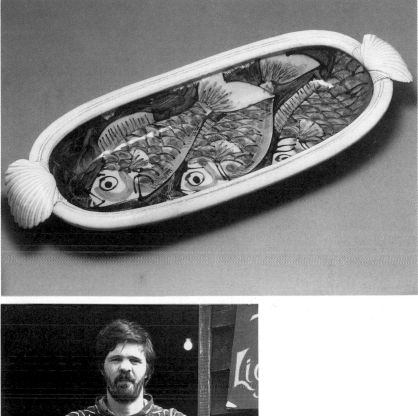

Bennett Cooper trained at Hornsey College of Art (Middlesex Polytechnic) 1971-74 and The Royal College of Art 1974-77. Set up present workshop in 1979. Working with high fired earthenware (1160°C). I produce a range of pressed and thrown highly decorative table and ovenware plus a few one off pots and some tile panels. Brightly coloured slips applied with trailer and brush enhanced with sgraffito and applied pigment enables me to work within the slipware tradition. The discipline involved in making decorative functional pots is a continual source of excitement and inspiration.

Emmanuel Cooper

Emmanuel Cooper Individual pots, mostly in porcelain, which include bowls and jug forms. Glazes tend to be bright and rich and include turquoise blues and green, nickel pinks and blues, uranium yellow. All are fired to 1260°C electric kiln. Has been making pots since 1965. Trained Dudley College of Education 1958-60, Bournemouth School of Art 1960-61, Hornsey School of Art 1961-62. Worked with Gwyn Hanssen and then Bryan Newman before opening own studio. Works alone. Co-editor (with Eileen Lewenstein) of *Ceramic Review*. Teaches part-time Middlesex University. Major exhibitions British Craft Centre, Boadicea, Craftsmen Potters Shop, J. K. Hill. Work in many collections including Victoria and Albert Museum, Royal Scottish Museum. Author of many books on ceramics including *New Ceramics* (with Eileen Lewenstein) *Glazes for the Studio Potter* (with Derek Royle (Batsford 1978) *The Potters Book of Glaze Recipes* (Batsford 1980) *A History of World Pottery* (Batsford 1988) *Electric Kiln Pottery* (Batsford 1982) *Cooper's Book of Glaze Recipes* (Batsford 1987) *Glazes* (Batsford 1992).

Gilles Le Corre

Gilles Le Corre Born in Quimper France, came to England in 1971 and trained at Camberwell School of Arts and Crafts between 1975-79. In 1982 set up a studio in Oxford building a gas kiln. 'My concerns about making this work has grown from a need to manipulate, reform and experiment with thrown forms so as to expand its possibilities. My new pieces contain the essence to function associated with movements of the sea, landscapes its textures and atmosphere, drawn from my links with Brittany.'

Dartington Pottery

Dartington Pottery is located on the Dartington Hall Estate in South Devon. The site was originally used by Bernard Leach as a Pottery in the 1930s. The association between Dartington Pottery and Janice Tchalenko as a designer is unique in contemporary studio ceramics; the pottery specializes in reduction stoneware. The bright colourful designs originate from a European rather than oriental tradition and in the '80s led a movement away from the more rustic styles that used to dominate studio pottery. Today the pottery is run by Stephen Course and Peter Cook and now employs about 12 people. There is a shop at the pottery and the work is available throughout the UK, Europe, the East and America. The pottery undertakes commissions for clients' specific designs, produces limited editions and tableware. The tableware is now produced under licence in Finland and will shortly be produced in China. The pottery operates an apprenticeship scheme.

Clive Davies

Clive Davies I enjoy making highly coloured and decorated reduction fired stoneware. I am constantly working on new glazes and at last have produced a yellow that is yellow every time. After years working in clay seven days a week I now have weekends off. Wonderful, and I still seem to get the same amount done. I make dishes, bowls, jugs, vases, large cups and saucers and tiles. The decoration is rarely the same. I have exhibited widely.

Derek Davis

Derek Davis Born London 1926. Studied Central School of Arts and Crafts 1946-50. Works in porcelain and stoneware. 'Artist in Residence' University of Sussex 1967. Exhibitions include: Primavera 1965, Liberty's 1966, Peter Dingley 1970, 81., Scottish Gallery 1986, 88. Sheila Harrison 1987, 88, 89., Amalgam 1973, Southampton 1974, Keramion Frechen, Germany, Blond Fine Arts London 1985, Castellamonte Italy 1991. Work represented in Victoria and Albert Museum, Paisley Museum Scotland, Garth Clark Collection Colorado U.S.A., Southampton Art Gallery, Keramion Frechen, Germany, Westerwald Keramick Museum, Germany.

Peter and Jill Dick

Peter and Jill Dick Coxwold Pottery is a small country workshop established in 1965 by Peter and Jill Dick. As in the early days they are now equal partners in the production of a wide variety of kitchen/tableware, planters and special commissions. At present the largest number of pots are thrown and decorated with brightly coloured slips inspired by the country pots of central Europe. This earthenware is electric fired. However, Peter Dick, who was trained by Michael Cardew and Ray Finch, still makes a limited number of platters and other more unusual pots which are fired in the big wood kiln to low stoneware temperatures. Jill Dick (trained at the Gloucestershire College of Art) is now using the recently installed propane kiln to develop her own distinctive range of stoneware. Coxwold lies in beautiful countryside 20 miles north of York. Visitors are welcome to look around the workshop and choose from the large selection of work in the Showroom. The Pottery Garden also sells splendid plant pots from other makers as well as those made by Peter and Jill Dick.

Mike Dodd

Mike Dodd Born 1943. From an early love of pottery, inspired by Donald Potter's tutelage at Bryanston, I decided to embrace the making of pots, after completing a medical degree at Cambridge University. I started my first pottery at Edburton in Sussex, armed with Leach's 'A Potter's Book' and very little else. At that time my knowledge was to say the least sparse. I did not know how to build a kiln or even to throw a lid. Twenty years later I am involved with my fourth pottery and am perhaps a little wiser. The dignity, conviction and freshness of form, being the very essence of pottery for me, is my main concern — and I have a preference for using materials for slips and glazes from the surrounding area, which, this time, happens to be the Lake District, granites, hornfels, andesites, irons, clays, etc. In 1979 I spent six months in Peru helping the Amnesha Indians to build a large wood-fired kiln and experimenting with local materials for glazes — a great experience. My work finds itself into many and various exhibitions here and abrorad.

Jack Doherty

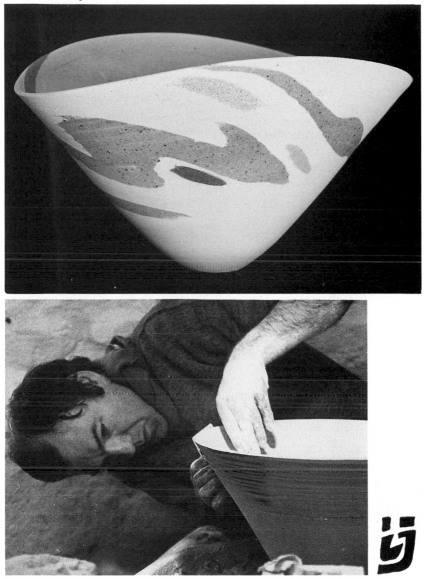

Jack Doherty 'My work with porcelain is wheel-based, with surfaces built up by inlaying strips of stained or textured clay during throwing. Often the forms are altered while the clay is still soft. Recently I have been firing with sodium vapour, experimenting with the iridescent surfaces sometimes produced when using minimal quantities of salt or soda. I have exhibited widely including the exhibitions at Faenza and Vallauris (awarded gold medals in 1974 & 1976) group shows in Scandinavia, Germany and the U.S.A. Recently my work has been shown in 'North of Watford Gap' the C.P.A. touring exhibition and in 'Trio' at the Peter Dingley gallery. My pots are in the collections of the Ulster Museum Arts Council of N. Ireland and Cheltenham Museum and Liverpool Museum.'

John Dunn

John Dunn His raku dishes stem from a decision to be single-minded about one particular aspect of ceramics and to eliminate all production which was not meaningful to him. Raku had always been held to be sacred and he refused to compromise in this area. After years of producing his 23″ diameter raku dishes for which he is known, he still surprised at the evolution and refinement which continues to take place. His technical problems are now resolved. His one remaining 'problem' is marketing, i.e. keeping pace with a seemingly endless demand. He believes that ceramics should be affordable and feels that his policy of moderate pricing has helped create this demand. Work has been featured in many exhibitions. It is distributed throughout Europe and housed in both public and private collections. Large decorated dishes are currently being introduced.

Geoffrey Eastop

Geoffrey Eastop trained as a painter at Goldsmiths' College, London and Academie Ranson, Paris. Over a long period has worked through a wide range of techniques.

At present making monolithic stoneware forms often painted with coloured vitreous slips; not as decoration but as an emphasis of character. Exhibitions include National Museum of Wales, Victoria and Albert Museum, London; Cologne and Stuttgart. Most recent solo exhibition: Contemporary Ceramics, London. Current major touring retrospective: Portsmouth City Museum Sept-Nov 1992: Newbury Museum Dec 1992-Feb 1993: Holburne Museum, Bath April-May 1993. Architectural commissions include large murals for Maudsley Hospital, London; Reading Civic Centre; Wall and floor tiles, Robinson College Chapel, Cambridge. Book: *The Hollow Vessel;* Bohun Gallery 1980. Fellow Society of Designer-Craftsmen.

Dorothy Feibleman

Dorothy Feibleman makes laminated coloured porcelain and parian ceramics including 22 and 18 karat gold and porcelain jewellery. Her fascination with using lamination is that the structure and decoration are integral. She makes ceramics fulltime and gives workshops and demonstrations. Her work is in many private and public collections including the Victoria and Albert Museum, the Indianapolis Art Museum, the Frankfurt, Darmstadt and Stuttgart Decorative Arts Museums.

Ray Finch

Ray Finch Trained with Michael Cardew 1936-39 and took over Winchcombe Pottery from him in 1946. Works with a team of five assistants, including son Michael, making wood fired stoneware. Many exhibitions.

Jutka Fischer

Jutka Fischer After training at the Central School of Art and Design, I set up a studio in 1977, and have been developing the technique of inlaid pots ever since. Work was interrupted for three years while I ran a gallery where I organised exhibitions combining two dimensional with three dimensional work. Now it is back to pots again, still using coloured bodies with inlaid decoration. I have shown work in galleries all over England, and have some pieces in public as well as private collections. I have no pottery mark but simply scratch my name into the pot somewhere.

Sylvia Des Fours

Sylvia Des Fours came to England from Czechoslovakia in 1949. Trained at Epsom and Hammersmith School of Art. Makes individual pieces in stoneware and porcelain, thrown with handbuilt extensions. Teaches at Richmond Adult and Community College; also at psychiatric hospital in Epsom. Believes in therapeutic value of working with clay and is deeply involved in matters of mental health. After a recent study trip to Japan delights in making thrown Ikebana pots.

David Frith

David Frith Born in 1943 trained at Flintshire, Wimbledon and Stoke on Trent Schools of Art. A full time potter since 1963, he moved to the Malt House in 1975, making stoneware and porcelain individual pieces some on a majestic scale. His present works stems from a continual development and an increased awareness and understanding for the materials. Increasingly the decorative motifs predominate with wax resist, brushwork and glaze trailing using celadons and iron glazes which are made and milled at the workshop. He holds the Brookhouse Pottery Schools and gives lectures and workshops in this country and abroad. Past Council Member and Vice-Chairman C.P.A., Index member of the Crafts Council. Work in many public and private collections.

Margaret Frith

Margaret Frith Born 1943, trained Bolton, Liverpool and Stoke-on-Trent Colleges of Art, joined David Frith at their first pottery workshop in 1965. For several years she was a production thrower and looks on this period as a vital training and a wonderful foundation for the individual porcelain pieces she now makes. She has developed the porcelain body for carved or coloured decoration. These designs are mainly floral, drawing beforehand, but liking to work directly onto the clay without copying as a greater spontaneity and flow is achieved. Holds the Brookhouse Pottery Schools each year with David and exhibits regularly in this country and abroad.

Tessa Fuchs

Tessa Fuchs Born Knutsford, Cheshire. Studied Salford Royal Technical College Art School, Central School of Arts and Crafts, London. Set up studio as an individual artist potter making sculptural pieces and some domestic ware in high fired earthenware using colourful matt glazes. Work inspired by her interest in animals, plants, gardening, trees, landscape and painting. She is also particularly influenced by her travels which have included China, Mexico and Kenya where she went on safari. Her latest work is on the subject of extraordinary exotic flowers and mythological and fantastic creatures. Many solo exhibitions. Work also shown in Victoria and Albert Museum: The Craftsmens Art, International Ceramics, Jubilee Exhibition, and other museums. BBC Television film 'In the Making' — twenty minute film featuring making ceramic landscape. Work features in various publications. Work in many museums and private collections. Video Tessa Fuchs 'Potters at Work' (PR Productions, Oxon).

Tony Gant

Tony Gant, working on his own, makes bowls, dishes, plates, wine and coffee sets, mugs and vases. Established 1961, 24 years in present studio.

Carolyn Genders

Carolyn Genders.

Carolyn Genders has always enjoyed drawing and painting. She constantly refers to her sketchbooks for inspiration when painting her handbuilt sculptural vessels. Using a wide range of vitreous coloured slips she approaches her work much as a painter does his canvas. The finished pieces have many of the qualities of a painting with the added excitement of constant surprise provided by the element of the three-dimensional. Born in Singapore, Carolyn trained at Brighton Polytechnic, 1975-1979, and at Goldsmiths' College, 1985-1986. In 1980 she set up her studio in the Sussex countryside. Currently teaching part-time and a visiting lecturer to various colleges and pottery societies. Her work is sold and exhibited widely in Britain, Germany, Holland and Japan and is represented in private collections worldwide.

John Gibson

Gibson

John Gibson Born Sheffield 1952; Chesterfield College of Art 1975-79. Worked with Josie Walter, Courtyard Pottery, Matlock 1979-86; from 1986-91 established two studios in Sheffield. In 1987 book *Pottery Decoration Contemporary Approaches* (A & C Black) was published. 'I have acted as visiting lecturer throughout Britain and abroad. Work is exhibited widely and found in public and private collections worldwide. In May 1991 my family and I moved to Bornholm, Denmark, a potters' island and famous for its beauty.

Christopher Green

Christopher Green Thrown porcelain bowls and plates fired in a reducing atmosphere. Particular interest in glazes using iron and copper for colour, and in kiln control. Born and educated in Zimbabwe. Training in Durban, South Africa and Goldsmiths' College, London.

Ian Gregory

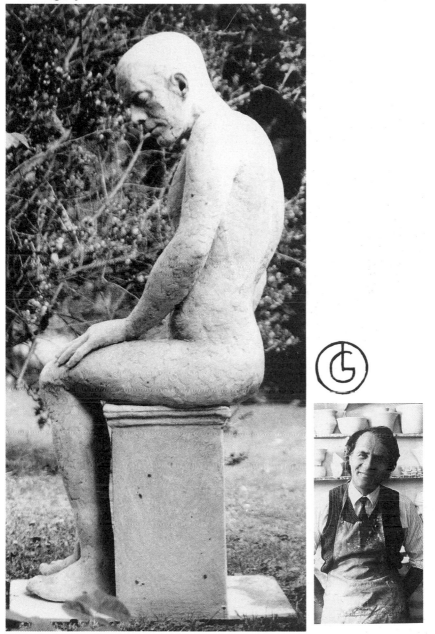

Ian Gregory Workshop opened in 1968 changing from earthenware to saltglaze in 1976. Elected to CPA in 1977 and served on the Council for two years. Commissioned by Pitmans in 1977 to write *Kiln Building* now in its second edition. Work is shown at Contemporary Applied Arts and many others. Examples of his work in many private and public collections worldwide. Guest teaching has been at Cardiff, Corsham and other Art Schools and now Head of Art and Design and Ceramics at Milton Abbey, Dorset. Currently producing life sized figurative sculpture and ash glazed vessels and finalizing a new book *Ceramic Sculpture* (A & C Black), publication autumn 1992.

Frank Hamer

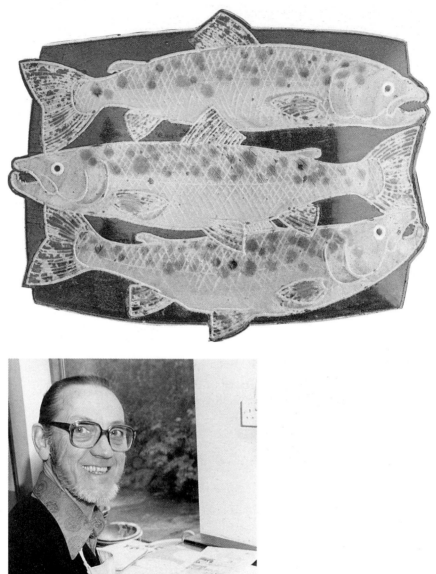

Frank Hamer press-moulds all his plates and dishes, and he rolls and hand-cuts decorative tiles. The plates and dishes are for wall display and special-use occasions. He has always enjoyed drawing and therefore decorates his work with observed recognisable images of fish, landscapes and flowers. The ware is reduced stoneware. Frank Hamer lives in rural Wales working in a studio which overlooks the Brecon Canal and where studio and kiln space are shared with Janet Hamer. He is co-author of *Clays* and *The Potter's Dictionary of Materials and Techniques*.

Jane Hamlyn

Jane Hamlyn All of Jane Hamlyn's work is raw glazed, once-fired, saltglazed stoneware, often with modelled handles and rouletting. The polychromatic effects achieved by the use of clay slips and glazes add to the vocabulary of surface elements and are enhanced by the dramatic effects of saltglazing, which characteristically renders each piece unique. Jane Hamlyn does not produce standard forms, preferring to allow herself the opportunity to change and develop. However, all the pots are made for use in a domestic setting. She finds the idea of function a stimulant rather than a limitation and sees the decorative and ornamental elements as integral to that function. In his recent book 'The New Ceramics, Trends and Traditions' (Thames and Hudson 1986) Peter Dormer writes of Jane Hamlyn's work 'She has found a way of quietly moving quasi-traditional pottery forward into a style appropriate for the modern kitchen or dining room.' Work in public collections: Victoria and Albert Museum and Crafts Council Collection, London, University of Wales Ceramics Collection. Aberystwyth, Hanley Museum, Nottingham, Usher Gallery Permanent Collection Lincoln, Cleveland Ceramics Collection Middlesborough, Sudbury Hall Collection Derbyshire and Newport Museum and Art Gallery Gwent.

Alan Heaps

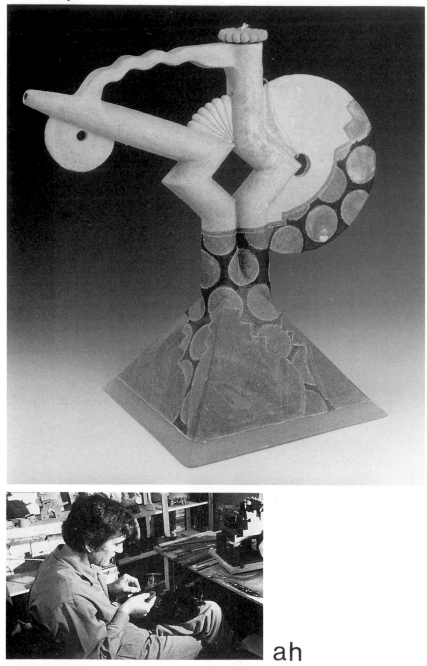

ah

Alan Heaps In the early 1960s Alan Heaps trained in Graphics at the Liverpool College of Art and has been making ceramics full time for the past twenty years, sixteen of which have been spent in his workshop in rural Mid-Wales. Each piece is individually hand built and decorated with slip and glaze stains using a matt glaze fired to 1140°C. He has exhibited extensively in Britain and on the continent of Europe and presently sells mostly in Germany.

Joan Hepworth

J. Hepworth

Joan Hepworth studied at Hastings School of Art for two years. While there won a scholarship to the Royal College of Art and entered the Design School to study mural decoration, fabric design and printing. After leaving college spent a year in a film cartoon studio before taking up teaching design and printing at Sutton School of Art. When pottery was introduced into the school she joined a class in her spare time and was taught by Harry Stringer and Brian Starkey. She became more and more enthusiastic over pottery and experimented with all methods of making pots. Eventually bought her own kiln and wheel and set up her own workshop. Finding she used the wheel less and less she decided after moving to her present address, to concentrate on slab pots and slip cast porcelain. Enjoys exploring and developing new shapes. Decorates mainly with ceramic crayons and some relief work. Uses an electric kiln firing to 1250°C. Finds the coloured crayons fade at higher temperatures. Has exhibited widely in this country with one-person exhibitions at Sutton School of Art and at Henley. Has also exhibited in Belgium, Austria and West Germany and sold to Japan.

Karin Hessenberg

Karin Hessenberg I graduated from Camberwell School of Arts and Crafts in 1974 and set up as a studio potter. I concentrated on making thrown, burnished and sawdust fired porcelain for many years. I began to find that throwing was restricting my ideas and in 1988, having been inspired by visits to India and Nepal, I began to make large hand-built pieces for the garden. I was encouraged in this development by an Individual Artist Award from Greater London Arts. Current work includes planters, stools, and ornamental heads for which I use Craft Crank clay and an ash glaze fired to stoneware at 1260°C. I make by slabbing, press-moulding, free-hand modelling and using impressed decoration. I have exhibited widely in Britain and abroad, and am on Crafts Council Index of quality. A number of museums have bought my work for their collections, including Glasgow and Stoke-on-Trent. My plant towers are featured in Malcolm Hillier's book *Container Gardening*. Recent commissions include a pair of tree contatiners for the Ferens Art Gallery in Hull. Examples of my work can also be seen in The Potters Garden in Garden Festival Wales, Ebbw Vale.

Joanna Howells

Joanna Howells Born in 1960 Joanna's first career was in medicine — she took a B.A. in Medical Sciences at Cambridge University. However, in 1984 she decided to pursue, full-time, her love of ceramics. She went to the studio pottery course at Harrow College, from where she graduated with distinction. She then set up her studio in London and has been exhibited widely since then.

Anita Hoy

Anita Hoy Mainly individual pieces, earthenware, stoneware, porcelain and some raku. Working alone. Trained at Copenhagen College of Art. Started and became head of studio departments at Bullers Ltd., Stoke-on-Trent, and Royal Doulton at Lambeth, working with porcelain and saltglazed stoneware. Looking for oneness of form and decoration, comprising: carving, coloured slips and oxide brushwork, under or over clear and opaque coloured reduction fired glazes at 1260°C. Work illustrated in books and articles (*Doulton Lambeth Wares* by D Eyles 1976 and *Studio Porcelain* by Peter Lane 1980). Retrospective Bullers exhibition at Gladstone Pottery Museum 1978 and Doulton Story at Victoria and Albert Museum 1979. Represented with a collection at Victoria and Albert Museum, and City Museum, Stoke-on-Trent. Taught for many years at West Surrey College of Art and Design. Now working at home. Work shown at the Crafts Council exhibition 'Influencial Europeans in British Crafts and Design', 1992.

John Huggins

John Huggins and his assistants, make a range of frost-proof terracotta plant pots. They range from small pots for window sills to large feature pots for gardens and patios. Most are thrown, some are handpressed. Many of his pots are decorated with a motif of the life-giving forms — the sun and the rain. He produces and sells a superb terracotta body blended from three local clays.

John Jelfs

John Jelfs Studied pottery at Cheltenham College of Art and set up present studio with wife Judy in 1973, making earthenware. Changed to stoneware in 1976. At present making a wide range of domestic ware and one-off pieces including some porcelain. Work sold through craft shops and galleries as well as from workshop.

Chris Jenkins

Chris Jenkins Born 1933. Trained as a sculptor and painter at Harrogate and the Slade School, finally as a potter at the Central School, London. I have been working with clay since 1957 in a variety of studios, currently in Marsden with a possible wood kiln in France. Essentially I produce a range of individual pieces fired to oxidised stoneware in an electric kiln, they are mostly decorated with slips using engraving and resist techniques. For some time I have been exploring the relationship between geometrical constructions and simple thrown forms, projecting two dimensional design onto three dimensional form.

Wendy Johnson

Wendy Johnson Since leaving Derbyshire College of Higher Education (1988-1990) I have been involved in the Nottingham Schools Studio Project. Whilst working as an Artist in Residence, I have been able to concentrate on my own work, developing aspects of form and colour. I am now in the process of setting up a workshop at home, as my residency is coming to an end. All of my work is handbuilt, using principally slabbing and modelling technique, based on heavily grogged white earthenware. After the biscuit firing the surface patterns are inlaid with oxides, to provide contrast. Bodystains and colour glazes are used, providing a blue colour palette. My range of work includes: clocks, candlesticks, vases, lidded boxes and various sized bowls.

Hazel Johnston

Hazel Johnston works in porcelain making thrown bottles and bowls. Clarity of form is very important and this together with subtly coloured and textured glaze surfaces are characteristic of her work. A dolomite glaze is used over various mixtures of metal oxides and a restrained use of gold lustre adds emphasis to some forms. All are fired in an 8 cu.ft. electric kiln. Trained at Manchester, N.D.D. 1st. class Hons., A.T.D. Taught at Mid-Warwickshire College and produced her own work, slipware, followed by domestic stoneware, then porcelain in the last twelve years. The present studio was set up in 1977.

David Jones

David Jones Born 1953. Graduated in Philosophy and Literature 1974. Like many potters in the early 1970s who tried the novel firing technique of (American) Raku — with secondary reduction — I was seduced by the flashes of brilliance occurring on an otherwise dull, thick, immature clay pot. The succeeding years have been an attempt at refinement and strategic control of glazing and firing, while retaining the aleatoric, random, element in the process. My influences have been substantially the philosophy of, and the objects collected and made for, the Japanese Tea-Masters. In recent years I have been pondering the vessels of the *English Tea-Ceremony* as well. Recent Exhibitions in England, Belgium and Germany. Currently Associate Senior Lecturer at Wolverhampton Polytechnic.

David Lloyd Jones

David Lloyd Jones Reduction fired stoneware and porcelain kitchen and tableware and other functional vessels. Some saltglaze.

Walter Keeler

Walter Keeler Functional pottery of an individual nature in saltglazed stoneware.

Ruth King

Ruth King trained at Camberwell School of Arts and Craft from 1974-1977 and established her own workshop in London in 1978. In 1981 she moved to York where she now lives and has her own studio. Her pots are handbuilt using various techniques of construction to produce individual decorated pieces in saltglazed stoneware. Ruth King has exhibited throughout Great Britain and has work in collections at Victoria and Albert Museum, Castle Museum Nottingham, Ulster Museum Belfast, York City Art Gallery and Museum of Scotland Edinburgh.

Gabriele Koch

Gabriele Koch Degree in English, History, Political Science at Heidelberg University. Studies and travels in Spain inspired me to want to work with clay. 1979-81 Goldsmiths' College Diploma in Art & Design, Ceramics. 1982 Crafts Council Setting-up Grant. Since then my work has been exhibited widely in the U.K. and abroad and is housed in many private and public collections including the Sainsbury Collection, Museums in Frankfurt, Karlsruhe and Lörrach, Art Galleries in Leeds and Gateshead, and the European Investment Bank in Luxembourg. All pieces are hand-built, burnished and subsequently smokefired.

Anna Lambert

AL

Anna Lambert.

Anna Lambert I set up my workshop after leaving Bath Academy of Art in 1980, first in Gloucestershire and since 1989 in Yorkshire. My work is all handbuilt earthenware, and although it is highly decorative I try to keep function an important element. Each piece is coiled, pinched or assembled from modelled parts, the form emerging slowly and incorporating influences from the local landscape, flora and fauna. I like to incorporate recently seen images with personal significance, working quickly to maintain a sense of immediacy. My underglaze painting is often influenced by the weather and season, thus springtime work is often full of fresh greens and thundery greys. I have exhibited widely in Britain and the U.S.A.

Nigel Lambert

Nigel Lambert Born in 1962, studied at Cornwall College of Further and Higher Education. After college I worked with Roger Cockram in his North Devon pottery. I set up my first pottery in Bristol; now I have a workshop in the Forest of Dean. I make a range of tableware, thrown and pressmoulded in earthenware fired to 1140°C. raw glazed and decorated with cobalt, iron and manganese and copper oxides, freely applied with brushes and fingers.

Peter Lane

Peter Lane Fellow of Society of Designer-Craftsmen (awarded Silver Medal 1981). Author of *Studio Porcelain* (Pitman 1980). *Studio Ceramics* (Collins 1983), *Ceramic Form* (Collins 1988). He has exhibited widely and given numerous lectures and demonstrations in Europe, Australia, New Zealand, Canada and the U.S.A. Most of his work is in porcelain (especially translucent bowls springing from narrow footrings) carved, incised and pierced or painted with ceramic stains. Represented in many public and private collections including the City Museum and Art Gallery, Stoke-on-Trent; Castle Museum, Norwich; Aberdeen Museum and Art Gallery; The Royal Scottish Museum, Edinburgh; National Gallery of Victoria, Melbourne, Australia; Utah Museum of Fine Arts, Salt Lake City, U.S.A.; etc.

Richard Launder

Richard Launder Improvisation is an ever-present element during making. This manner of approach is linked with the constancy of calculated risk. Exploring the areas of expression/concept which are concerned with Function, Vessel and Sculpture. Feeling no conflict in the fluid overlaps of these categories: necessitating an intensity, a shift, of concentration. Using metaphor, symbol, illusion. The essential act of actualizing from the ephemeral. Working with the possibilities available in high temperature saltglaze 1300°C (of colour, texture, mark, structure) from a purposefully limited material choice. Studied ceramics at W.S.C.A.D., Farnham (1972-76). Has worked and exhibited widely in England, Greece and Scandinavia both as a ceramist and lecturer, and is represented in a number of private and public collections. Currently Associate Professor of Ceramics at the National College of Art Craft and Design, Bergen, Norway. Works in England for half the year.

David Leach

David Leach started in 1930 with father, Bernard Leach, as a student, manager and partner at the Leach Pottery, St. Ives until 1956. Now after 62 years potting works alone on thrown stoneware and porcelain, mostly commissions and individual pots. Prices range from £5 to £500. Exhibits regularly in the United Kingdom, U.S.A., Japan and the Continent in group or one man shows. Work in many national and continental museums. Past chairman of the Craftsmen Potters Association and council member of the Crafts Council. Late external assessor for studio pottery courses Harrow School of Art, Scottish Education Department and other colleges of art. Initiated Dartington Pottery Training workshop 1975 with the late David Canter. Gold Medallist Istanbul 1967. One time Head Ceramics Department Loughborough College of Art 1953-54. Spends part of each year giving lectures, demonstrations, workshops chiefly in U.S.A., Canada and on the Continent.

Janet Leach

Janet Leach was born in Texas U.S.A. in 1918. Moved to New York to study sculpture. Began studying pottery in 1948. Met Bernard Leach, Shoji Hamada and Soetsu Yanagi when they toured America in 1952. Went to Japan to study under Hamada in 1954. In 1956 came to England to marry Bernard Leach and now runs the Leach Pottery in St. Ives, Cornwall making her own individual pots. Likes using several different clays and firing techniques — all reduction stoneware. Has held regular one-person exhibitions in England and Japan and her work included in many national and international shows and collections.

John Leach

MUCHELNEY

John Leach I established Muchelney Pottery, Somerset in 1964 with my wife Lizzie and family. Looking back over almost 35 years' potting I feel indebted to my father and grandfather, to Ray Finch and Colin Pearson, who were instrumental in forming the ideas and themes of pottery which I still embrace. I did not have a formal art school training, but have grown out of a strong workshop tradition, disciplined in the production of functional pottery. Not until 1983 did I feel able to free myself from the limitations of this work ethic to produce signed individual work exploring a wider range of shapes and creative impulses. Examples of this work are always available in the pottery shop alongside our classic range of wood-fired kitchen stoneware. The pottery team consists of Lizzie and myself as partners, Nick Rees whose contribution to the repeat stoneware production and the day-to-day running of the pottery is vital, and our able student, Mark Melbourne.

Eileen Lewenstein

Eileen Lewenstein makes individual pots and objects in stoneware and porcelain. The sea and its ability to both wear away through constant motion and yet also built up through barnacles and mussels on partially submerged breakwaters and rocks provides a constant fascination. Recent work has included paired forms; thrown and altered porcelain and coiled stoneware. Exhibited widely in this country and abroad including Portugal 1990, Australia 1988, U.S.A. 1983, 1985; New Zealand 1983; Yugoslavia 1984, 1985 and Istanbul. Represented in many public and private collections including Victoria and Albert Museum; Glasgow Art Gallery and Museum; Museum of Decorative Arts, Prague; Museum of Contemporary Ceramics, Bechyne, Czechoslovakia; Villeroy and Boch Sculpture Park, Mettlach, West Germany; Auckland Institute and Hawkes Bay Art Gallery and Museum, New Zealand. Co-Editor Ceramic Review. Co-Editor with Emmanuel Cooper *New Ceramics* Studio Vista 1974.

Martin Lewis

Martin Lewis Born 1953 Altrincham, Cheshire. Educated at S. E. Berkshire College, Windsor, Berks. and Chesterfield College of Art and Design. Most of the work is centred around that overworked phrase 'The Vessel', but it still holds my attention for all that. The pots are handbuilt and the surface worked using layers of painted slips and glazes with up to five firings at various temperatures. Work in private and public collections including Contemporary Arts Society (Paisley Museum); Nottingham Castle Museum, Leicester Schools and the Bergen and Trondheim Museums, Norway. Exhibited in U.K., Norway, France and Switzerland.

Mal Magson

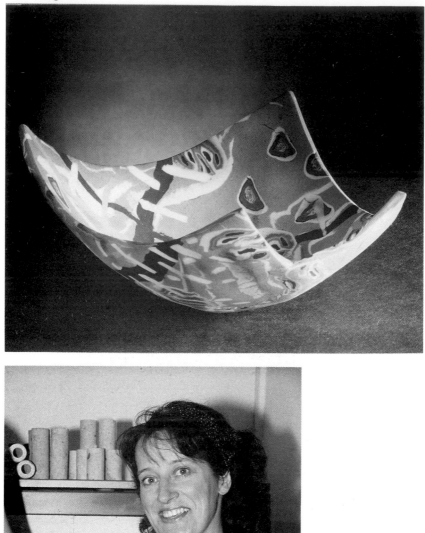

Mal Magson started work in 1972 from a home-based studio. Work has been widely exhibited and collected both here and abroad. Has taught full-time at University College, North Riding College, Scarborough since 1987 producing work patchily in the interim. Presently engaged in establishing a suburban workshop where exploration of the agateware technique using stained, laminated clay continues. Forms are moulded from rolled and cut slabs, clay used is white stoneware and porcelain fired to 1260°C. Recently the patterning has been concerned with overlap, intersection and fragmentation influenced by a fascination with worn textiles and eroded mosaics, frescoes and tiles. The interpretation features patches, stitches and seams.

John Maltby

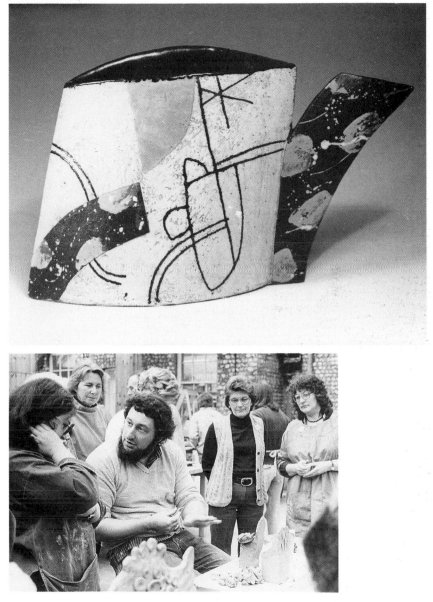

MALTBY

John Maltby trained as a sculptor. He worked with David Leach for two years before starting his own workshop in 1964. Since 1976 he has made only individual pieces mainly in reduced stoneware. The sources for work have been English land and seascape — mostly handbuilt, decorated with coloured slip glazes involving three separate firings. His work is in many public collections and he lectures widely in the U.K. and abroad. Recent solo exhibitions have included Heidelberg and Munich in Gemany, and Galerie Besson in London.

West Marshall

West Marshall studied pottery at Harrow School of Art and set up his first workshop in Norfolk in 1970. During the seventies he made reduced, stoneware domestic ware and some slip decorated, one-off thrown pots. He now lives in Buckinghamshire and produces small quantities of enamel decorated, porcelain, domestic ware. He currently teaches at Harrow.

Will Levi Marshall

Will Levi Marshall At present I am working, studying and teaching at Alfred University, New York. Although I enjoy it a great deal in America, I intend to return to the U.K. in 1993. I hope the photograph shows my work is utilitarian. I try to make pots that 'are function' rather than pots 'about function'. I believe there is a difference. For many years I have been involved in atmosphere kilns (salt, soda and wood), however I am currently exploring glaze and slip colours together with overglaze enamels. This has meant more use of gas and electric kilns and allowed me to indulge my interest in brushwork. I try to create a multi-layered image to give depth to the pot's surface. The creative process is full of surprises for me and I hope to keep finding new stones to turn.

Leo Francis Matthews

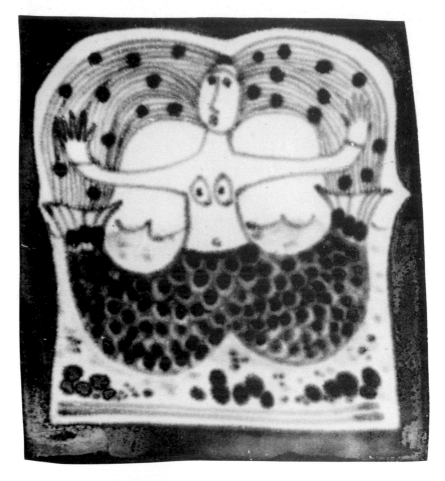

Leo Francis Matthews studied graphics at Manchester College of Art and ceramics at Stoke-on-Trent College of Art. Lectured on ceramics for over twenty-four years at various major colleges of art in Britain. Produces sculptural ceramics, murals and some domestic studio pottery.

Peter Meanley

pm 92

Peter Meanley Since 1987 my output has been almost totally limited to the manufacture of individual teapots. All teapots are salt fired at Cone 10 and capable of use. Ideas are based upon things seen, and my conscience, that of wanting to produce the very best and looking closely at fine historical examples (not necessarily teapots). Presently Senior Course Tutor: BA Hons. Fine Craft Design, University of Ulster at Belfast.

Eric James Mellon

Eric James Mellon Born 1925. Studied Watford: Harrow: Central School of Arts & Crafts, London. Creates brush drawn decorated ceramic fired 1300°C. using tree and shrub ash glazes. Represented in the Victoria and Albert Museum and collections in Britain and internationally. 'Drawing onto clay is firing thoughts into ceramic. The concern is not academic correctness in drawing but to create a WORK of visual decorative poetic surprise, and aesthetic satisfaction.' Photograph (above) Theme of Tenderness. A personal mythology on the moon goddess, mermaid and bird-maiden, and human lovers. The lion symbolises rebirth and the bi-cycle eternity. Bowl 26cm diameter. See: Rogers, P *Ash Glazes* (Black/Chilton 1991) and 'Magic and Poetry'' *Ceramic Review* Number 114.1988.

Jon Middlemiss

Jon Middlemiss Studied Fine Art at Scarborough & Exeter Colleges of Art. After five years of producing functional ware, established Chantry School of Art in 1977 as a community of artists running courses and seminars in crafts and meditational subjects. Since 1979 has exhibited widely in major galleries in U.K., Belgium, Holland, Germany, France and the U.S.A., including touring exhibitions. Has lectured and demonstrated in California with the A.C.C.A., American Ceramics Society, and at colleges. Also as Invitational exhibitor at the Centenial celebrations of the Industriegewerkeschaft-Chemie-Papier-Keramik, Hannover. Work has been featured in ceramics magazines, catalogues, dictionaries and other books in the U.K., U.S.A., and Germany. The gallery Keramik-Studio-Middlemiss was established in 1990 in Gelsenkirchen, Germany. Work has won awards in Germany and Holland, and is in many public and private collections and museums. Member of Crafts Council Index, 1989.

'My current work has been influenced by several trips to New Mexico & Arizona to study the ceramics of the Pueblo Indians of the Rio Grande. The contrasting geometric qualities and spiritual philosophy add to the foundation of my work in meditation and visualization on the Cabalistic Tree of Life.' Most pieces are thrown and slabbed with applied engobes, underglazes, matt glazes and lustres, multifired in oxidation to 1180°C and 1290°C.'

David Miller

David Miller Born in London. Studied sculpture, printmaking and ceramics at Ravensbourne and Brighton Colleges of Art. Set up workshop in London in the 1970s. Now living and working in Southern France making one-off pieces and a small range of highly decorated functional ware based on traditional French slipware. Exhibitions in France, Holland, England and Germany.

Ursula Mommens

Ursula Mommens I learnt for two years under William Staite Murray at the Royal College of Art and much later had the great good luck of working with Michael Cardew at Wenford Bridge. I started off converting an old cowhouse in Kent and after marriage to Julian Trevelyan worked at Durham Wharf Hammersmith Terrace, London. I now work at the pottery I set up 37 years ago in South Heighton, Newhaven making useful stoneware using mainly wood ash glazes on our own body — fired in Chris Lewis's big woodfired kiln or my small oil one.

Emily Myers

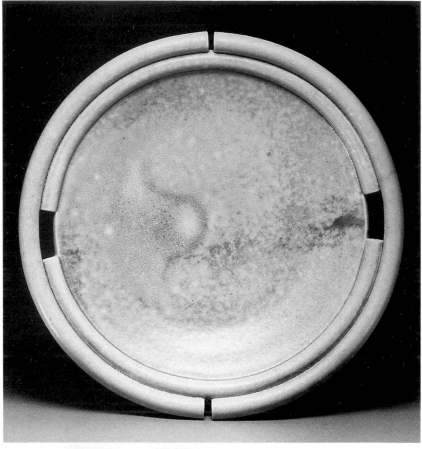

Emily Myers My stoneware ceramics are distinctive for their strong controlled forms and the intensity of their glazes. The work shares certain qualities with metal — clean uncompromising lines and a matt surface. Throwing, press-moulding and extruding are combined to make dishes, vases and candle-holders. I received a Crafts Council Setting-up Grant in 1990 and have exhibited regularly at the Chelsea Crafts Fair. Exhibitions to date include The Ceramics Series show at Aberystwyth Arts Centre (April 1992). My work may also be seen at Wilson and Gough and The Crafts Council Gallery Shop.

Laurence McGowan

Laurence McGowan Born Salisbury 1942. Set up own workshop in 1979 after earlier career making maps and interpreting aerial photos in various parts of the world. Trained at Alvingham and with Alan Caiger-Smith, Aldermaston. Traditional majolica decorative techniques employed on quiet, wheel thrown functional forms. Various stain and oxide mixtures painted on zirconium opacified Cornish Stone based glazes. Electric fired to cone 8 (1260°C). Decorative motifs taken from plant and animal forms, applied to both enhance the pot's form and reflect something of the exuberance of nature. Interests relating to work include lettering/calligraphy and the decorative arts of the Islamic world.

Susan Nemeth

Susan Nemeth Born 1957. Bournville School of Art 1973-75. Wolverhampton Polytechnic, B.A.(Hons.) 1975-78. One-off, handbuilt, highly decorated bowls, plates, vases. 13cm - 40cm dia. 1280°C. Vitrified. The theme of food is used as inspiration for a new series of plates, platters and bowls, thus creating 'dishes' such as 'Crab with Lotus Root' and 'Pearl-studded Pork Balls'. Pieces are made incorporating these images in an abstract or patterned way, with emphasis on colour, using layers of coloured porcelain inlays, slips and stains. Sanding between firing gives a smooth matt finish. Susan has exhibited widely in Britain and Japan, America and Germany, and has work in Ulster Museum, University of Cardiff collection and the Leicestershire Collection for Schools and Colleges. She is also on the Crafts Council Selected Index.

Magdalene Anyango N Odundo

Odundo
1992

Magdalene Anyango N Odundo Handbuilt low fired burnished and reduced ceramics. Works chiefly for exhibitions and commissions.

Lawson Oyekan

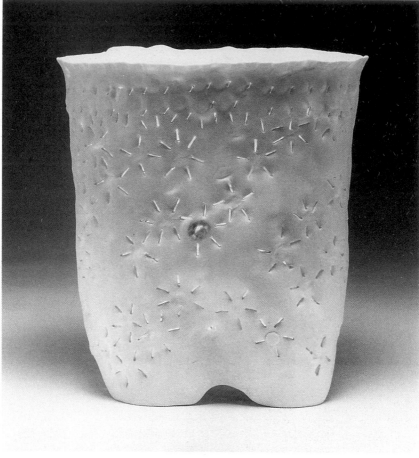

LAWS

Lawson Oyekan Within the disciplines of throwing and handbuilding, I have examined the formal values of both movement and endurance using a variety of clays though generally porcelain for throwing and crank for handbuilding. I also make my own glaze colours using natural metal oxides. My work reflects the merging and influence of both my Nigerian roots and my European experience. I am constantly exploring forms and colour from both cultures while being drawn to particular themes of light and movement as derived from each. My current work concerns light and survival.

Colin Pearson

Colin Pearson Born London 1923. Studied painting at Goldsmiths' College. Makes individual pieces in porcelain and stoneware. Winner of the 33rd Grand Prix at Faenza, Italy, and in 1980 was awarded a major Crafts Council Bursary for study in the Far East. Part-time lecturer at Camberwell College of Art. Has work in many public and private collections. Does regular workshops and slide presentations in the U.K., on the Continent, U.S.A., Malaysia and Australia. A member of the International Academy of Ceramics, and on the Crafts Council Slide Index. Vice Chairman of London Potters.

Jane Perryman

Jane Perryman trained at Hornsey College of Art and later spent a year at Keramisch Werkcentrum in Holland. My pots are handbuilt, using a combination of coiling, press moulding and slabbing techniques, inspired by African and Early Celtic pots. They are covered with coloured slips, burnished, fired to 980°C and then treated with various forms of resist and fired in sawdust. I exhibit regularly both in England and abroad and my work is in private and public collections. Presently serving on the Council of the CPA and writing a book *Smoke Fired Pottery* for A & C Black.

Richard Phethean

Richard Phethean trained at Camberwell, graduating in 1976, and in the Studios of Colin Pearson and Janice Tchalenko making reduction fired domestic stoneware. An interest in slip-decorated terracotta began with traditional tools and techniques and evolved into a more personal style significantly influenced by a two year period working in Papua New Guinea as a crafts project volunteer. Range of work includes the classic thrown vessel forms made as individual pieces and limited editions or commissions of tableware, on sale in shops and galleries nationwide. Author of *Throwing* (forthcoming) in 'The Complete Potter' series, pottery teaching experiences at all levels includes private tuition in throwing given regularly in his garden studio.

Anthony Phillips

Anthony Phillips makes slip-decorated earthenware. The emphasis is on function and he makes a range of tableware including teapots, cups and saucers, bowls and plates. More fanciful are his jugs, thrown and assembled, jars, vases and large bowls. Most of the work is thrown in red earthenware clay, decorated in a variety of coloured slips by sponging, brushing and trailing, and finished with a clear glaze. 'My pottery is made to be used, but I also want it to be visually pleasing and challenging. Throwing and slip-decorating are exciting techniques because they give so much scope for form and design.'

Peter Phillips

Peter Phillips trained at the Royal College of Art. He works with his wife Julie making a variety of decorative and domestic pieces in stoneware and porcelain. These are fired in a 12 cu.ft. gas kiln to cone 9. He makes his own glazes which vary from matt to shiny, stained with oxides. Peter and Julie also have a studio in France (Dordogne) with an oil fired kiln which he built himself with the help of friends. Peter holds classes both in Kent and in the Dordogne.

Mick Pinner

Mick Pinner My formal training was undertaken at Kidderminster and W.S.C.A.D. in Farnham between 1977 and 1982. I then spent two years at Wrecclesham Pottery where I learnt repetition throwing and the production of large terrracotta garden pots following the illness and death of Reg Harris. In 1984 I moved to Hampshire and the workshop then occupied by Nigel Wood who has given invaluable technical advice over the years. I make terracotta garden pots, mostly large, attempting to combine traditional and imaginative techniques with the inherent properties of the material always in mind. A similar attitude oversees the firing, where much of the decoration is created.

John Pollex

John Pollex Trained Harrow College of Art 1968-70. Assistant to Bryan Newman and Colin Pearson 1970-71. Present workshop established 1971. Author of *Slipware* (Pitman 1979). My work is made with a buff-earthenware clay and glaze fired to 1100°C in an electric kiln. Since 1990 I have been altering the shapes of my pots whilst they are still soft; this makes each one unique. The coloured slips are applied with a variety of sponges and brushes. From 1979 I have given over forty seminar-demonstrations in the U.K. and overseas. I particularly enjoy this aspect of my work as it gives me the opportunity to travel and meet fellow potters. Many solo and group exhibitions.

Vicki Read

R. CLAYCUTTERS.

Vicki Reed started her first pottery in Winslow, Bucks. in 1962, after helping to teach pottery in evening classes with John Marlow and Helen Walters. Is a founder member of the CPA and an honorary member of the International Academy of Ceramics. The last two of many exhibitions were in the Southampton City Museum and Art Gallery and the County Museum in Aylesbury, Bucks., in a major exhibition of twentieth century potters. 'I still enjoy making very large pots and platters and 'Swan pots', with the traditional 'block design' of oxide underglaze, for which I am known — also a range of domestic ware. I work in stoneware clay, to fire to 1280°C.in a reducing atmosphere. Am currently setting up my new pottery in the Village Forge, at 'Church Green', Brickleigh, near Tiverton, Devon.'

Mary Rich

Mary Rich At present all work is made of porcelain, mostly decorated with liquid bright gold and various lustres.

Christine-Ann Richards

CAR CAR

Christine-Ann Richards Trained at Harrow School of Art and Technology (1971-73) under Mick Casson. Worked for Bryan Newman and David Leach. Started own workshop with Barbican Arts Group (1975-83). I now live and work at home. The 1978 CPA trip fo China had a radical effect on my work and way of life. Since then I have studied Chinese art, taken people to China and continued developing my own work. While continuing to work in thrown porcelain I have recently begun making large vitrified earthenware vessels suitable for interiors, conservatories or the garden, some of these have incorporated water features. Work in public and private collections. Exhibited in England and abroad. I work alone.

David Roberts

David Roberts Coil built, Raku fired vessels. Well known large work recently augmented by smaller scale pots partially inspired by early bronze age Cypriot ceramics. Work exhibited widely throughout the U.K. and abroad and is represented in many public and private collections including the Victoria and Albert Museum, Ulster Museum and the Museum of Wales.

Jim Robison

Jim Robison produces a range of sculpture and functional work. Large scale, slabware, colourful ash glazes and rich surface details are recognized trademarks. The Yorkshire landscape, with its patterns of green fields and dry stone walls, is a primary source of inspiration. American born and trained, he moved to Holmfirth and established his present studio in 1975. He exhibits widely in the U.K. and abroad and has completed numerous commissions for architects and landscape designers. Current activities include special interests in architectural murals and garden sculpture.

Phil Rogers

Phil Rogers Most of my pots are thrown and are then fired in either the 65 cu.ft. downdraught reduction kiln or a 35 cu.ft. catenary salt kiln (soon to be replaced with a bigger version). I make extensive use of ash glazes in both kilns. Started making pottery in 1971 and began working in present workshop in 1985. Our series of summer workshops continue in the converted stone barn overlooking the upper Wye valley. Have exhibited widely in the U.K. and abroad and work is included in many public and private collections around the world, notably, The National Museum of Wales, Newport Museum and Art Gallery, University of Wales Collection, Aberystwyth, Bill Ismay Collection, Llantarnam Grange Collection, Dyfed, Powys and Gwent County Councils and a number of private collections in Japan and the U.S.A. Author of *Ash Glazes* (A&C Black 1992) and currently chairman of the Craft Potters Association.

Duncan Ross

Duncan Ross established his present workshop near Farnham in 1989, after a period of study and exploration into terra-sigillata techniques and firing methods. Working with burnished earthenware and terra-sigillata slips he has developed a range of individual forms which are classical in feeling. He aims to achieve a sense of balance with surface patterns that repeat and move in curves and sweeping lines. These surface textures are built up using inlayed and resisted layers of fine slips, the work then being saggar fired and strongly smoked to produce a range of colours from light orange to greens, greys and black.

Fiona Salazar

Fiona Salazar

Fiona Salazar Trained at Central School of Art and Design 1976-78 and Royal College of Art 1979-82. Low fired earthenware, one-off handbuilt pots made by coiling method. Painted and burnished slip using stains and oxides, wax finished.

Antonia Salmon

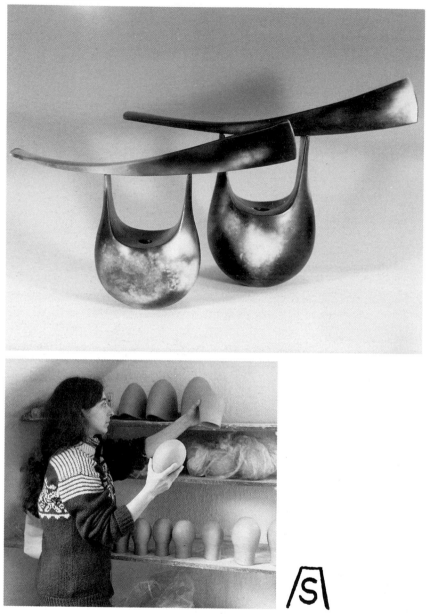

Antonia Salmon Born in London 1959. Studied Geography at Sheffield University and then Studio Pottery at Harrow 1981-83. 1984 spent in the Middle East and India. From 1985-89 my first studio at the Barbican Arts Group, London. In 1989 I moved to live in Sheffield. The range of work includes sculptural pieces, dishes and vessels, all characterized by my interest in classical forms, ethnic sculpture and the landscape. I use stoneware for throwing and handbuilding. Decoration; oxides, relief carving, incising is integral to the simple forms and to their final firing in sawdust. Work is exhibited throughout Britain.

Patrick Sargent

Patrick Sargent studied wood firing and trained at Farnham (W.S.C.A.) under Paul Barron and Henry Hammond 1977-1980. Still training. Established present workshop in Emmental in Switzerland in 1989. Woodfires a five cubic metre single chamber cross draught climbing kiln with demolition timber to 1320°C. Firings lasting 50 to 60 hours. Most work is thrown, using momentum wheels and clay is prepared by foot. The wide variety of surface qualities are achieved more as a result of the intensity and duration of the firing, the style of setting in the kiln and the deposit of ash than from a conscious attempt to formally decorate. Exhibits and demonstrates in the U.K.

Micki Schloessingk

Micki Schloessingk makes wood-fired saltglazed pots.

David Scott

D.S.

David Scott Born in Yorkshire, trained Stoke on Trent and Royal College of Art. 'The work swings between more or less straightforward variations on functional themes and the production of individual pieces of a less conventional nature. I work as a full time lecturer in charge of the Ceramics Department at Loughborough College of Art and Design, and this involvement both restricts and influences the way I work. I exhibit frequently in Britain and Europe.' Work in public and private collections including the Victoria & Albert Museum, Norwich Castle Museum etc.

Ray Silverman

Ray Silverman Trained at Camberwell School of Art and Crafts, London and University of London Goldsmiths' College. Lecturer at Newham Community College, London, teaching Design, and at University of London Goldsmiths' College teaching Ceramics. Fellow of the Society of Designer-Craftsmen. On the Crafts Council Index. Solus Exhibitions: including Victoria and Albert Museum, London. (Man Made Series); Exhibitied widely in group exhibitions throughout the world. My work has ranged from thrown tableware, handbuilt pieces to working as a designer in the ceramic industry. Over the past 15 years I have devoted the time in my workshop to producing individual thrown forms in porcelain and stoneware.

Michael Skipwith

s

Michael Skipwith Lotus Pottery was founded in 1957 by Michael and Elizabeth Skipwith who had first met as students at Leeds College of Art. From 1957-1979 they ran the pottery, employing up to 17, making coloured glazed domestic ware fired in electric kilns. In 1981 after conversion of part of their large old farm and letting off much of their premises as workshops, Michael recommenced potting on his own — making stoneware in a wood fired kiln. He currently specialises in plant pots particularly liking the colour which the flames give to unglazed pots. He is the Devon stockist for Potclays range of clays and raw materials.

Alison Small

Alison Small At college, slipcasting became a strong feature within my work. The idea of using slipcasting as a method of manufacturing jewellery originated from a final degree year project. The forms emerge after a process of modelling and shaping plaster. Patterns and markings are applied to the inside of the mould. The base colour is poured in, transferring the pattern from the plaster to clay. The pieces are bisque fired to 1000°C and after drilling, fettling and filing, the pieces are fired to 1220°C with a two and a half hour soak. The surface is then polished to give a smoother, sensual feel. The silverwork is designed to be an extension of the piece, exaggerating and accentuating the form and the findings are attached by the technique of riveting — this allows a certain amount of free movement to the jewellery when worn. Work has appeared in a number of exhibitions.

Frank Smith

Frank Smith Born Sydney Australia 1927. Worked in partnership with my father on nursery in N.W. Kent growing plants and flowers. Moved to a small farm in 1950. Began making pots in 1962 using wood to once-fire pots to stoneware. Worked as assistant to Colin Pearson for a year in 1966. Taught for six years in adult education. Moved to present address in 1976. Using catenary arch trolley hearth oil-fired and LPG kilns. Still making stoneware, porcelain and garden pots. Will take paying students on a weekly basis. Has exhibited in Germany for the past ten years.

Peter Smith

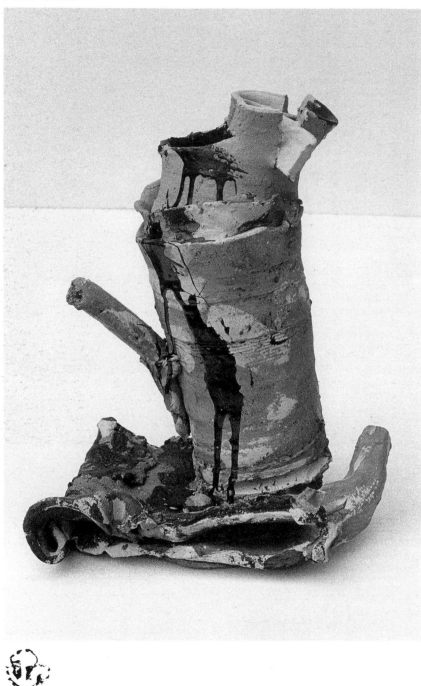

Peter Smith Formerly a research chemist specialising in high temperature chemistry. Started Bojewyan Pottery in 1975. At present making both ceramics and sculpture.

John Solly

John Solly born Maidstone 1928. Started making pots at Maidstone School of Art in 1945 under the guidance of Percy Brown and later Gwylym Thomas. After National Service in the RAF went to the Central School of Art where Dora Billington headed the pottery department. Spent very short working period with Wally Cole at the Rye Pottery, and Ray Finch at the Winchcombe Pottery. Set up the pottery in Maidstone in 1953, and made-slipware and high fired earthenware. In 1960 he began to run regular 'summer schools' at the pottery, and to date, over 1350 students have attended. He was one of the founder members of the CPA and has been a full member ever since. He was the founder chairman of the Kent Potters Association and is a Fellow of the Society of Designer-Craftsmen. He is now continuing to produce slipware and high fired earthenware, both domestic repetition and more colourful individual pieces. Selling direct from the workshop, exhibitions, and from the CPA. After 33 years at the pottery in Maidstone, the Sollys moved to Peasmarsh in May 1986.

Peter Stoodley

Peter Stoodley Makes unglazed, inlaid slip decorated stoneware planters, fired in an electric kiln. Studied painting at Bournemouth and at Goldsmiths' Schools of Art. Took Art Teacher's Diploma at the London Institute of Education in 1947 and during that year chose pottery as a craft subject together with bookbinding at Camberwell School of Art. In 1948 started the Pottery Centre at High Barnet and taught there for two years. Returned to Bournemouth in 1950 and worked in the making shop at Poole Pottery for one year. Began teaching part-time at the Bournemouth College of Art in 1951 and remained there in various capacities until retirement in 1980. Set up first workshop at Ferndown, Dorset in 1952. Built coke and drip feed oil kilns and throwing wheel and used clay dug off the moor. Started making thrown domestic ware and plant pots, some of which were exported to New Zealand. At that time received first commission for large planters, made by coiling, and the making of such pots has remained primary concern ever since. During the years 1957-63 was associated with Saviac Workshops in building and development of the original Saviac geared wooden framed kick wheel and numerous gas and electric kilns. Moved workshop to Bournemouth in 1963 and built electric kiln still in use. Joined CPA in 1958. Moved home and workshop to Lymington in 1987, situated in the middle of an Iron Age Hill Fort about a mile from town.

Harry Horlock Stringer

Harry Horlock Stringer One of the 1950s wave of 'Painter turned Potter' who had to teach themselves, he found a new way of understanding the formulation and making of glazes without resort to the use of molecular formulae. Always very interested in teaching, he built a school, literally with his bare hands. This was opened in 1965 and has catered for a large international summer school ever since. An interest in Raku in the late fifties led to the first book on the subject to be written in the West in 1967 also designing and making an electric Raku kiln safe enough to use in the classroom in 1965. Being confined to the use of electricity only, much research has gone into the development of quality in oxidising atmospheres, this led to the discovery of the first 'Reactive Slip' in 1975. Served for nine years on the Council of the Craftsmen Potters Association during its formative years and was Editor of their journal for a number of years. He continues to contribute to potters' journals. In the fifties he had a workshop in the old Fulham Pottery making once-fired earthenware for domestic use later transferring to Taggs Yard where twice fired earthenware was made. At present stoneware and a small amount of porcelain, mostly for domestic use is produced. Work has been exhibited in a number of different countries where it is in museums and private collections. He was head of an art department in a Teacher Training College for many years and lectures at home and abroad by invitation.

Helen Swain

Helen Swain I make individual forms in all clays, now preferring thrown and burnished, or part-glazed, earthenware and handbuilding. Studied Willesden School of Art (1945-1951) painting then pottery and terracotta; grateful for the time teaching I had there in the training of eye and hand. After N.D.D. I spent three months in Cornwall with Harry and May Davis, a wonderful experience, leaving to do A.T.C. at Hornsey College of Art. Then three happy years, working with Agnete Hoy, for Royal Doulton (Lambeth). I learned so much from Nita, hand carving and brush painting, with saltglaze mainly. Since 1963 I have been teaching at Goldsmiths' College, London. As a founder member of CPA I had a solus exhibition in 1961 and have contributed to 15 groups since then.

Sutton Taylor

Sutton Taylor lives in Yorkshire and he uses local clay for his lustre pots, local limestone, marl and fireclay. Lustre is a glamorous method of glazing which derives from Middle Eastern and Moorish potters and travelled through Spain and Italy to England. He summarises his firing process as follows: Biscuit firing to 1000°C glaze firing to 1150°C lustre firing to 750°C with on-glaze pigments including silver, gold, copper or tantalum in wood smoke reduction atmosphere. If underglaze slips and engobes, which combine the above metals, are applied to the unfired clay or the biscuit the glaze firing is cooled under reduction firing. Lustre finishes are very difficult to control, for instance they are affected by humidity and atmospheric changes. Sutton Taylor's output is small but his pots have a rich and sombre lustre unlike any others and are keenly collected by museums as well as private buyers. Has exhibited widely both in UK and abroad.

Sabina Teuteberg

Sabina Teuteberg has a fine-art background and trained in ceramics at Croydon College of Art and Design. Decorates mainly clay slabs with coloured clay inlays and slips. At present the colourful abstract patterned slabs are turned into a range of functional ceramics by the method of jigger and jolley. All work is high fired earthenware. Work has been exhibited and sold throughout the U.K. and abroad. Example of work in public collections: University of Wales, Cleveland County Museum Service, Ulster Museum, Crafts Council Collection.

Owen Thorpe

Owen Thorpe studied at Willesden Art School (1951-56), Harrow School of Art (1959-61) and Bournemouth College of Art (1961-62). Set up workshop in Ealing, London 1970. Moved to Priestweston, Shropshire 1975, Churchstoke Powys 1981. Works alone. Produces a range of domestic stoneware pottery using coloured and locally occurring slips and wax-resist decoration. All work is wheel-thrown and is fired with electric oxidising firing. Also produces range of garden pottery decorated with coloured slip brushwork as well as highly decorated individual pieces using a technique like majolica but at stoneware temperatures. Tin glazes are employed, some tinted cream or light blue, with elaborate brushed patterns applied to the unfired glaze. Has exhibited widely.

Vera Tollow

Vera Tollow I have moved again. Having I thought settled in Goudhurst, I then married and now live in an oasthouse on an apple farm in Hawkhurst. My new studio is near completion and soon my usual range of domestic as well as individual stoneware pots will be coming off the wheel. My bottled-gas kiln which was built at Goudhurst will be moved over shortly. Knowing, as I do, that apple tree ash makes an interesting glaze, the farmer here had better beware in case I am tempted to chop down one or two of his trees.

Marianne de Trey

Marianne de Trey Born in London of Swiss parents and trained at the Royal College of Art. Widow of potter and painter T S Haile. After many years running a workshop and producing domestic stoneware at Dartington, she now works almost entirely in porcelain, hand thrown and decorated with coloured slips. She was an early member of the CPA and is on The Design Index.

Judy Trim

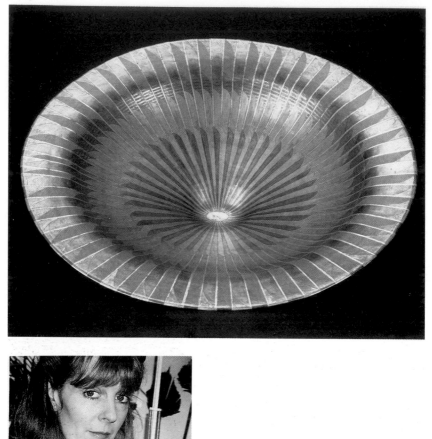

Judy Trim Born in Cambridge. Trained at the Bath Academy of Art, Corsham 1961-64 specialising in painting and ceramics. From 1974 onwards taught as visiting lecturer at various art colleges including Wimbledon, Croydon, Belfast and Bath Academy of Art. Since 1980 have been in many group and solo exhibitions in England and the U.S.A. Work can be found in private and public collections both here and abroad, including The British Crafts Council Permanent Collection, The Paisley Museum, Scotland and the Los Angeles County Museum of Art, U.S.A. Bibliography includes The International Design Year Book, Decorative Processes by John Gibson, and many others. I generally make individual coiled vessels which are non-functional and of a contemplative nature. These range from simple to decorated forms. Materials and processes involve T-material and red clay, lustres, coloured slips, smoking and sgraffito. The essence of these works draws inspiration from a range of cultures, classical or arcane, whose ritual functions are abstracted within such forms as 'tear jars', 'offering bowls', 'funereal vessels'.

Ruthanne Tudball

Ruthanne Tudball Born in California, U.S.A. Post-Graduate Diploma in Ceramics from Goldsmiths' College after years of being mainly self-taught and after gaining an honours degree in English and a Post-Graduate Certificate in Education. All of my work is stoneware, raw glazed, slip decorated and once-fired sodium-glazed with sodium compounds other than salt. My main concern is with the clay and the pleasure of manipulating it during throwing. I want to make forms that capture the soft plasticity of the material and have both dignity and a lively freshness. Sodium glazing can have dramatic effects on the surfaces of the pots emphasizing the making process and path of the flames across the work, rendering each pot unique. I make my pots to be lived with, handled and used.

Tina Vlassopulos

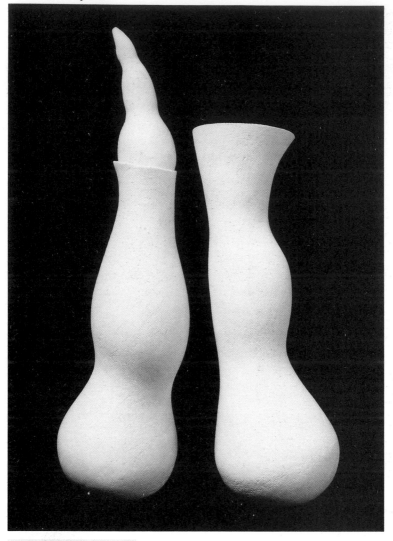

Tina Vlassopulos Individual pieces in stoneware using coloured slips or burnished red earthenware.

Alan Wallwork

Aw W.

Alan Wallwork born Watford 1931. First workshop Forest Hill, South London 1957 influenced by teaching of Kenneth Clark and Gordon Baldwin at Goldsmiths' College. Worked in earthenware — thrown domestic ware and handbuilt forms — also tiles. Moved to Greenwich in 1960 and Marnhull, Dorset, in 1964 now working mainly in stoneware. His work was distributed worldwide, selected by the Design Centre and for public and private collections, including the Victoria and Albert Museum and Kyoto Museum, Japan. In the '70s, tiring of the artificial pressure of exhibitions and sharing the growing concern with energy conservation and pollution he experimented with alternative materials and firing methods, selling his work directly or through local galleries with a relaxed atmosphere. Inflation at the end of the '70s clinched his decision to wind down quantity production and he moved to Lyme Regis in 1984. The dramatic setting of his first workshop there had practical disadvantages and he has now moved across the valley to the hamlet of Rocombe, above Uplyme. Most smaller pieces are formed directly in the hand, usually from two or more pinch pots joined in various ways. This method helps to produce forms which invite exploration by touch, qualities of weight and texture being as important as the purely visual. A variety of clays are used, often one layered over another, often with materials which burn out during firing, leaving pitted, cratered surfaces. the kiln is propane reduction fired to temperatures in excess of 1300°C. His forms, colours and textures have an affinity with those found in the coast and countryside of Dorset — the cool, bleached colours and weathered, eroded surfaces of the seashore — the swelling, sensuous forms and warm colours of seedcases, fruits and shells.

Josie Walter

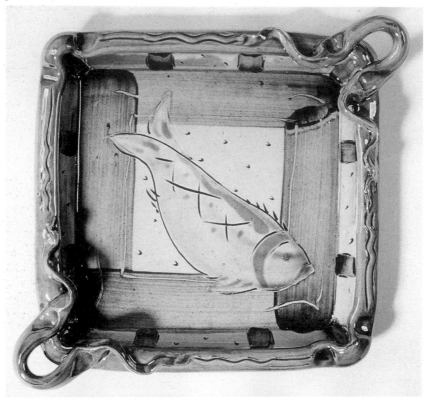

· Walter ·

Josie Walter Born 1951. Trained as an anthropologist, then as a teacher, and finally as a potter on the Studio Ceramics Course, Chesterfield College of Art 1976-79. Spent an invaluable 6 months as a repetition thrower with Suzie and Nigel Atkins, Poterie du Don Auvergne, France. Shared a workshop with John Gibson for 8 years and then moved to an old mill for the next 6. Is now working at home for the first time in a newly built workshop. Over the past few years I have experimented with combinations of paper resist, colour infill and slip trailing (first cutting and then tearing the paper to give a softer effect). However, feeling that the images had become too static and dense, I have been exploring the qualities inherent in my materials. Pouring the slips thinly to create overlapping layers and to let the red earthenware body show through, and using the marks of the brush, highlighted with sgraffito, has created a greater sense of movement and a fresh perspective. All the work is once fired and to Cone 03.

Sarah Walton

Sarah Walton Saltglazed sculptural pieces for outside. These pieces replace the pots I used to make. They connect with the landscape drawing and painting I started in my teens and have done since.

John Ward

John Ward Born in London 1938. Studied ceramics at Camberwell School of Art and Crafts (1966-1970). Set up first workroom in 1970 and taught part-time at an adult education institute until 1979 before moving to Wales to pot full time. Central theme is simple hollow forms, function being secondary to form. Pots are fired in electric kilns — biscuit firing to 1000°C, glaze 1250°C. Glazes are applied by a combination of spraying, pouring and painting, sometimes with banded decoration beneath. Four main glazes are used, all matt; white, black, blue/green and brown/black; recently blue and ochre have been added. Solo exhibitions in U.K., Germany and U.S.A.

Sasha Wardell

Sasha Wardell Born in 1956 in Sri Lanka. Studied ceramics at Bath Academy of Art (1976-79), North Staffordshire Polytechnic (1979-81) and Ecole Nationale d'Art Dècoratifs, in Limoges, France. Have taught in various art colleges since 1981 and set up workshop, exhibiting widely in the U.K. and abroad since 1982. Moved to France in 1989 and re-established workshop near Brive-la-Gaillarde where now running summer courses in plaster work and slip-casting. Materials and processes involve slip-casting bone china to an egg-shell thinness to enhance translucency. Models are produced by plaster-forming techniques using a turning lathe and hand-carving. After moulding, the pieces are fired 3 times. This includes a soft-firing, after which the work is sanded, a 1260°C firing to mature the body, and finally, a 1080°C firing to harden on the decoration, which is airbrushed through a series of intricate masks.

Robin Welch

Robin Welch His individual pots are coiled and thrown in stoneware clay, and after refining the form by turning and scraping, slip is added to the still wet surface to produce a striking texture, this together with some raw glazed areas is then fired to high temperatures. Coloured glazes are added and each is fired to fix it to the body. A pot may have as many as six firings, each being a lower temperature than the previous one. some of the brightest coloured glazes are added last. His work has been shown throughout the world and is included in museum collections in Great Britain, Holland and Australia, including huge candle holders for Lincoln Cathedral.

John Wheeldon

John Wheeldon Born 1950, trained at Chesterfield College of Art and Design and the Polytechnic Wolverhampton 1969-1974. 'I use resinate lustres on black basalt and porcelain forms. As a contrast to using stamps, I am increasingly decorating using resists and brushed lustres. I am also getting more involved in techniques using multiple firings combined with solvents to disrupt the lustre surface. As an alternative to all this disciplined pattern-making I am experimenting with raku — enjoying it for its directness and the necessity to submit to a less controllable process.'

David White

David White My work is predominantly reduced porcelain with crackle glazes. I have produced a range of glazes which craze in various ways, varying from no craze to a very fine one. Colour is achieved by combining oxides and glaze stains. The glazes are then blended by carefully controlled spraying using up to five glazes on a pot. On cooling, the pots are transferred to an electric kiln at 100°C to stop the crazing while each pot is then examined in turn and allowed to cool or dunked in cold water until a desirable crackle is achieved. Blended waterproof inks are then brushed into the crackle and washed off with cellulose thinners.

Mary White

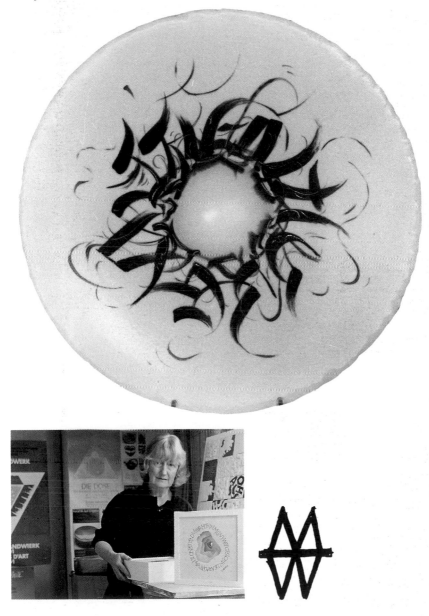

Mary White Trained at Newport School of Art, Hammersmith School of Art and Goldsmiths' College. Initiated the Ceramic Workshop in Atlantic College 1962-1972. Set up in 1972 and worked, self-employed, with painter husband Charles. In 1980 moved to West Germany to be in the 'middle of Europe'. Live in wine-producing village. 'Formerly my work was mainly organic, using porcelain, often with bodycolour. Now my early interest in Calligraphy has returned and I am experimenting with ways of using this in combination with ceramics. I have exhibited widely and my work is in many important Museums and private Collections. Awarded Rheinland-Pfalz Staatspreis in 1982 and other international prizes followed. Represented in many international magazines, catalogues and books.'

David Winkley

David Winkley Born 1939. Originally trained as a painter at the School of Fine Art, Reading University and at Pembroke College, Cambridge. After a brief period in Bristol, he moved in 1966 to West Somerset where he now makes an exceptionally wide range of stoneware pots for everyday use together with individual pieces in stoneware and porcelain. Firings are in a 230 cu.ft. two-chamber oil-fired kiln. Currently writing a book on contemporary functional potters to be published in 1994.

Mollie Winterburn

Mollie Winterburn All my work consists of individual pieces. I have Walls, Heads, Journeys, Candlesticks, Houses, Crosses and many others. Besides I keep a constant store of Bottles. As always I am happy working in this beautiful and lovely place.

Mary Wondrausch

Mary Wondrausch I work in earthenware using a honey glaze for the more traditional slip-trailed pots. I specialize in individually commissioned commemorative plates, which we post world-wide. Lettering is a major preoccupation. Cheese platters from 9"-16" form the balance of my work, decorated in the sgraffito manner, enhanced with oxides under a clear glaze. The subject of my gouache paintings is often reflected in the central decoration of these platters.'

Gary Wood

Gary Wood 'My ideas come from a number of different sources; amongst these is a liking for primitive African sculpture, and primitive ulitarian or ritualistic objects and architecture. For me, the aim when making is to create an object which gives back a feeling of presence and life. I try to combine strong forms with interesting surface qualities using different clays, slips and glazes. I make bowls, teabowls, stools, jars and vases in stoneware and porcelain.' Born in Bradford, West Yorkshire in 1955. Studied ceramics at Cumbria College of Art and Design, 1984-86. First workshop in Carlisle, 1986-90. Elected Fellow of Contemporary Ceramics in April 1990. Received Northern Arts Craft Award and Northern Arts Travel Award in 1991. Numerous exhibiitons including: Bettles Gallery, Hampshire, 1990; David Holmes Gallery, Halifax, 1991; CPA New Members Show, London, 1991; Masterworks Gallery, Auckland, New Zealand, 1991. Work in numerous collections.

Nigel Wood

Nigel Wood Trained at the traditional country potteries of S&E Colllier, Tilehurst, Reading, and A. Harris & Sons, Wrecclesham, Farnham, Surrey. Learned big-ware throwing. West Surrey College of Art & Design, Farnham (1969-1972). Established Meon Pottery, West Meon, Hampshire in partnership in 1973. Worked at West Meon, making stoneware, porcelain and large garden pots from 1973-1984. Long-standing interest in Chinese ceramics led to the writing of *Oriental Glazes* (Pitman Publishing 1978). Have since published some thirty papers worldwide on the technology of Far Eastern ceramics and bronzes (presented papers in China in 1982, 1985, 1989 and 1992). Presently consultant to Far Eastern departments of the Victoria and Albert Museum and the British Museum. Also lecturer on ceramic technology at the Royal College of Art, Central St. Martins, West Surrey College of Art and Sotheby's Educational Studies. Still making ceramics when teaching and research allow.

Steve Woodhead

Steve Woodhead I started potting in 1980, I am mainly self taught but attended several summer workshops by David Frith and recently Phil Rogers. In 1991 I was elected Fellow of the CPA. All my pots are made on the wheel, many of the shapes and forms have been inspired from traditional Korean pottery which complements the floral decoration. Biscuited pots are glazed and the decoration is built up on top of the glaze using a variety of pigments and glazes. My decoration is inspired from the image of a typical English country garden, with flowers flowing wildly over formal trellis work. The pieces are finally fired in a 70 cu.ft. gas kiln to around 1300°C. I use the Harry Davis body which I prepare in a dough mixer and de-airing pugmill. This gives me a superb throwing body. In addition I prepare all my glazes and pigments from raw materials as this enables me to control the quality.'

Gary Wornell

Gary Wornell Canadian born. Studied ceramics in Stoke on Trent and set up his studio in Suffolk in 1976. working primarily in terra-cotta using burnished slips. Winner of the INAX Design prize in 1991. Works in the U.K., France and Japan as well as lecturing in ceramics at the Hong Kong Polytechnic and the University of Industrial Design, Helsinki. Exhibitions, Tokyo, Boston U.S.A., Helsinki, Victoria BC, and throughout Europe.

Rosemary Wren and Peter Crotty

Rosemary Wren and Peter Crotty follow the tradition in which potters, since prehistoric times, have constructed animals and birds with their normal pot-making techniques — keenly observed but following the demands of the material. They use no means of repetition whatever, so that each piece has individual personality. Rosemary and Peter have a considerable following amongst collectors. They are currently endeavouring to set up their workshop in the spectacular Scottish Highlands — ceramically expressed as porcelain collage landscape bowls — following 10 years in Devon after leaving Surrey where Rosemary's parents set up The Oxshott Pottery in 1920. See her book *Animal Forms and Figures* (Batsford 1990).

Caroline Whyman

Caroline Whyman started art school intending to become a painter, but work with clay convinced her to become a potter. She studed at Camberwell Art School where there was a strong bias towards studio pottery, and was one of the last group of students to be taught by Lucie Rie and Hans Coper. At her first workshop at Camden Lock, she worked for nine years with stoneware and porcelain, throwing domestic ware, coiling large planters and slabbng vases and boxes. As an urban potter, she used an electric kiln developing colourful glazes as an alternative to tenmokus and creams. She likes porcelain because the white body brightens coloured glazes; she also enjoys the precision with which it can be turned and thrown. At her second workshop in Islington she developed more one off pieces. After visiting Japan in 1980, and inspired by the textile design, Caroline developed an interest in decoration, using coloured slips and paper resist. Now in her third workshop in South London, she throws porcelain sometimes using underglaze blue decoration and precious metal lustres, a direct result of a recent trip to India where the vibrance and strength of the colours and textures made a lasting impression. She shares her workshop with a group of young potters who are able to have access to a well equipped studio. 'Whilst the space is limited, it is supportive and stimulating to work with other potters.'

Takeshi Yasuda

Takeshi Yasuda trained at The Daisei Pottery, Mashiko, Japan (1963-65). Worked in U.K. since 1973. Exhibits widely.

Joanna and Andrew Young

A & J YOUNG GRESHAM

Joanna and Andrew Young Dip. A.D. Ceramics at W.S.C.A.D. Farnham, Surrey, 1970-73. Worked in France with Gwyn Hanssen for 6 months. A.T.C. Goldsmiths' College, London 1974. Set up workshop, 1975 in Hunworth, North Norfolk. Interest was, and still is to provide interesting and practical everyday pots in a repeated range. Most pots are wheel thrown, some are shaped later by cutting and squaring in various ways. The main glaze is thinly applied, and once fired under reduction in a 100 cu.ft. gas kiln. The finish is often mistaken for salt glaze. 1981, moved to large workshop at Lower Gresham, Norfolk. Continued production with two assistants. The pots are sold to some shops and also through own shop next door to workshop. Occasional exhibitions, Crafts Council Bursary 1988.

Monica Young

Monica Young Born Paris 1929. Left France 1941. Studied painting at Ealing School of Art (NDD. ATD) and at the Escuella Superior de Bellas Artes, Barcelona. Earned living by painting and book-illustration until 1972 when she began to teach herself to coil pots. In 1974 she established a permanent workshop in North Yorkshire. Makes large stoneware pots and ceramic sculptures, maximum height: 5'. Their surfaces are textured and of a deep toasted colour. All pieces are coiled using crank clay and are fired to 1300°C in a reducing atmosphere. The high temperature together with the drainage hole provided ensures that a piece will withstand normal winter outdoor temperature. She exhibits widely in the United Kingdom and her work has been bought for public and private collections in England, America, Canada, Nigeria and Japan.

Illustrated Directory of CPA Professional Members

A full list of Professional Members, together with their addresses, can be found on page 262

Billy Adams

Billy Adams 'I am essentially an Irish potter, now living and working in Wales. My pots are handbuilt, usually from a thrown base, working upwards in several stages. Three different sorts of clay are used — an interior layer of 'craft crank', an intermediate layer of clay mixed to prevent shrinkage of the pot during firing, and an outer surface of porcelain which is encouraged to buckle and crack as I shape the form from inside the pot. This retains a fine hard texture, rather than becoming friable. At a midway stage I introduce a stylistically intrusive form such as a regular circular thrown handle or a smoothed rim — to represent the intervention of humans in the natural world.'

Marilyn Andreetti

Marilyn Andreetti Trained at Farnham School of Art 1966-69. 'I taught art and design for more than ten years before deciding to buy a kiln and make pots at home in the spare bedroom. I now work in a small converted coach house. My work varies; I have made individual oxidised stoneware pieces based on architecture, but most of my present work is plates and dishes, either thrown or press-moulded in red clay. I decorate with underglaze colours on a cream slip background. The pots are bisque fired to 1000°C in an electric kiln. I enjoy making colourful, decorative, commemorative yet functional ware. I sell through exhibitions, craft fairs, and from the workshop.'

Elizabeth Aylmer

Elizabeth Aylmer 'I regard myself as self-taught but in fact was generously instructed by a friend who had not only been to art college but also served a rigorous apprenticeship at Denby with the original classical throwers, thus for many years speed and precision were my goals. This was a good discipline and enabled me to produce large quanitites of ware at reasonable prices. Having been raised in Zimbabwe my influences are drawn from African culture and this is instantly recognisable both in my domestic ware and the individual pots that I make when time allows.'

Sylph Baier

Sylph Baier Trained in Germany and West Wales. Attended Dyfed College of Art 1981-84 and is currently working in Brighton as part of a mixed disciplined group studio. Produces various ranges of domestic ware using slips, sgraffito and majolica techniques.

Richard Baxter

Richard Baxter

BAXTER

Richard Baxter Born 1959. Studied ceramics at Loughborough College of Art finishing in 1981. Established first workshop with Crafts Council setting up grant. 'Most of my output is domestic earthenware — bold forms, simply decorated. I fire to 1100°C in an electric top loading kiln. My one-offs explore sculptures that question the function, the relationship between inner and outer space, time/ageing processes and the point where the 'making' stops. Archaeological finds, primitive architecture, nature and geometry all contribute to the forms alongside marks developed from the making process — throwing, stretching, compressing, breaking.'

John Berry

JOHN BERRY

John Berry Born London 1925. Studied Architecture and Painting at the Polytechnic of Central London and Central St. Martins. During 1950s employed as painter/designer at Seviers and the Sun Pottery, London. Since 1986 lives and works in London and France. Work, including also prints, drawings and collages, in the collections of the Tate Gallery; Victoria and Albert Museum, Imperial War Museum; Museum Sztuki, Poland; Hope College and Wooster Art Museums, USA; Museum of Wales; Welsh Arts Council; KLM (Holland) etc. 'Currently my pots are handbuilt individual pieces, usually relating to the figure, decorated with coloured slips and glazes in white stoneware.'

Suzanne Bergne

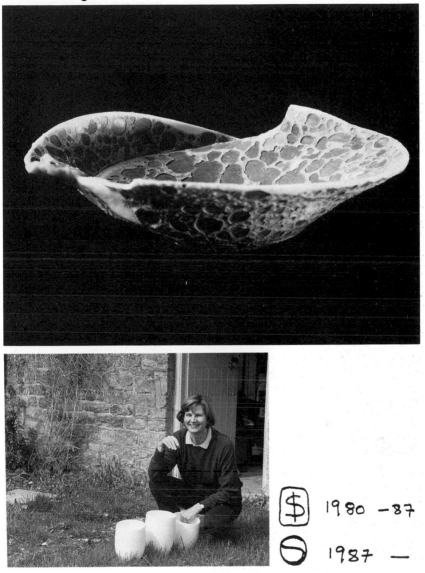

$ 1980 -87

⊖ 1987 —

Suzanne Bergne Born in Upper Silesia, studied literature and philosophy at Munich and Vienna Universities (1958-63). She travelled and worked for 20 years mainly in the Middle East. 1977-80 she trained formally as a potter at Croydon School of Art and Design, followed by seven years of working and teaching in Athens and Hongkong. Finally, in 1987, she settled in London with a studio in Gloucestershire. She makes porcelain bowls and containers on the wheel and uses them as the canvas for coloured glazefields juxtaposed by various pouring methods. Recently she developed a way of altering the exactly thrown forms so that the dynamics of throwing and glaze pouring are emphasized. Hand in hand with an interest in watercolour technique and life drawing, glaze effects are developed that capture the soft edge quality of the first and the rhythm and volume contemplated in the latter. She sells on a regular basis through shops and galleries in UK, Germany and Japan. Her work is represented in the Victoria and Albert Museum, Hongkong Museum of Art and the Hongkong Tea Museum.

Gillian Bliss

Gillian Bliss Born in 1955. Began potting in 1979 after BA (Hons) Ceramics at Cardiff College of Art. All work is thrown in porcelain and finely turned, producing both functional ware and one-off pieces. The individual pieces are decorated with natural motifs, using the technique of sgraffito to reveal the white clay beneath coloured slips. Further colour is added with glaze. Each pot is divided into areas of decoration to give a feeling of pattern, as well as showing drawings of fish, birds, plants etc. Exhibitions with the South Wales Potters and Makers Guild in Wales.

Keith Booth

KB **KB**

Keith Booth After studying ceramics at Hornsey College of Art, he set up his first workshop in London in 1975 and then moved to Maidstone in 1981. He enjoys using a variety of forming techniques and manipulating texture, form and glaze finish to create his distinctive individually produced pieces. He works mostly with oxidised stoneware firing to 1260°C. His work is in collections in the UK and overseas.

Richard Boswell

RICHARD BOSWELL

Richard Boswell 'Scraping surplus clay away after hours of inlaying, revealing the crisp decoration as an integral part of the form, never fails to exhilarate. I experiment with new tools, extending the vocabulary of marks which can be made in the leatherhard clay. New coloured bodies and decorating slips extend the possibilities even further. The challenge is in putting all the elements together, and knowing when to stop. The transparent glazed earthenware is etched after glazing which gives the work its characteristic 'feel'. My workshop and showroom is in the picturesque setting of Emsworth Mill Pond, overlooking the harbour.'

David Brown

David Brown 'Over the years I seem to have maintained an unswerving obsession with the teapot. I guess it is the duality of function and aesthetic allied to the potential for sculptural fantasy, so much a part of the history of the teapot which elevates it to the position almost of an ikon, and which continues to present the perpetual challenge. I am interested in organic growth and decay, deterioration, fragmentation encrusted, textured surfaces and in the relationship beween organic form and machinery. My teapots naturally reflect these current concerns. I also make a range of practical, thrown and inexpensive, domestic stoneware pots.'

Jenny Browne

Jenny Browne 'From 1974-77 I attended the Ceramics Course at Chelsea School of Art. I then set up a studio in Battersea making thrown domestic ware which I sold at Covent Garden market for several years. During this period I taught at an adult institute in Stepney Green. At present I am making individual pieces, wheel-thrown in white stoneware fired to 1200°C. The decoration is dictated by the shape of the pot and gradually evolves using a combination of brushwork and sgraffito on coloured slips.'

Tony Carter

Tony Carter Tony started the pottery in 1978 with his wife Anita and quickly became known as one of the original 'fun ceramic' studios, then known as Kiln Cottage Pottery. Today (1992), Carters Ceramic Designs has become internationally known for its highly collectable teapots which are handmade at the original premises in the heart of Suffolk at Debenham. The work from the pottery is sold to retailers in the U.K. and worldwide, with approximately 50% of the production being export sales.

Tom Chamberlain

Tom Chamberlain 'Started pottery at the age of fourteen whilst I was at school as a means of whiling away the long weekends. My pottery skills are largely self-taught with the aid of books and the occasional course. Most of my work is thrown with platters and bowl forms predominating. I am now concentrating on reduced, decorated stoneware using a smooth, white body and celadon type base glazes. All work is decorated with a variety of pigments and coloured glazes painted and trailed over the base glaze. I am currently interested in the effects of making up large motifs from small repeated units and the interface between bowls and platters. All my work is biscuit fired to 1000°C and then glaze fired to 1300°C in a small gas kiln. My work is continually changing with numerous glazes tests always in progress. In addition I am experimenting with applied handles and the cutting and rejoining of the leather hard pieces but the physical properties of the clay result in a high proportion of cracks occurring; problems which I have yet to overcome with any great success. I work during the weekends and evenings from a converted garage in our garden.'

Trevor Chaplin

Trevor Chaplin trained as a teacher in the early 1970s, studying design and pottery. Taught for 17 years. 'I am now potting full-time at my home in the Wiltshire countryside. I produce a small number of sculptural pieces together with a growing range of domestic ware; mainly thrown. All my work is high fired reduction stoneware. My particular interest at the moment is making large bowls and exploring altering basic forms by manipulation, faceting, cutting, folding etc., to achieve the effects I am searching for. My pottery is very much inspired by natural forms with strong traditional elements. I exhibit in both Oxfordshire and Wiltshire.'

Linda Chew

Linda Chew was born Winchester 1951. Studied sculpture at Cheltenham College of Art 1970-1973. Workshop experience, and a year at London University for Art Teachers Certificate, was followed by teaching in Winchester whilst setting up my workshop. 'My ideas are influenced by a love of textiles, and the movement of patterns. The handbuilt bowls and dishes I make are constructed from slabs of clay, usually T-material, porcelain or crank, impressed with lace, haberdashery, netting etc. After the pieces are assembled, patterns are embellished with slips, oxide washes over wax resist and glazes. Work is fired to 1260°C in an electric kiln.'

Desmond Clover

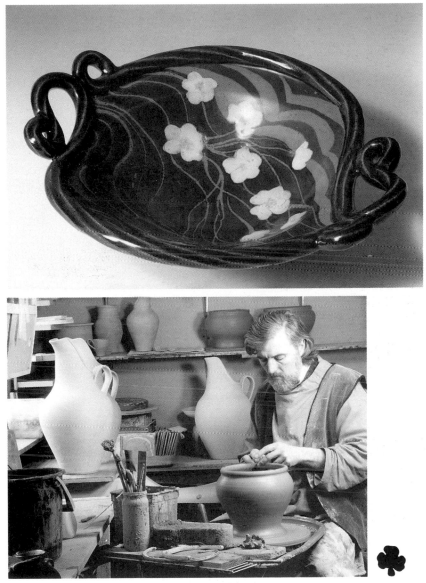

Desmond Clover 'My pots are thrown, some changed by cutting and adding rims and handles. I use a combination of abstracted and representational images and create depth within the surface of the vessel. I decorate with coloured glazes I have developed over the years. I like to build up the design like a painting, brushing, dipping and using wax resist, keeping it fresh as possible. They are fired to stoneware temperature in a reduction atmosphere. My pots range from mugs, tableware to more individual pieces all decorated in unique designs.'

Elaine Coles

Elaine Coles 'I have been a potter for 16 years making a wide range of reduced domestic stoneware, as well as some highly decorated one-off pieces, including large bowls and platters. The decoration is glaze in bright patterns freely applied with slip trailers, stencils sponges etc. Originally I was self-taught but in 1987 I spent a year at Goldsmiths' College on a Diploma Course where I concentrated on mould making and slip castings, some of these techniques are incorporated in my work. In 1990 I opened my present workshop together with my assistant Jennie Gilbert where we have a large workshop showroom selling a full range of our products.

Jo Connell

Jo Connell Studied ceramics at Staffordshire Polytechnic, and taught full-time for several years before setting up own workshop. Current studio established 1991 in the old bakehouse of listed Georgian house on the old Roman road, Watling Street (A5). Produces a range of decorative unglazed stoneware with inlaid surface pattern using coloured clays ranging from pastels to black. The range comprises largely vessels and bowls, combining press-moulding and hand-building methods. Some raku also, and Roman-style mixing bowls, as made in this village from 1st Century AD.

Molly Curley

Molly Curley trained at Cardiff College of Art. After teaching art and ceramics for twenty years, started potting full-time in 1982. Having trained as an illustrator, decorative ware evolved inevitably: slip-decorated earthenware, with some stoneware, all wheel-thrown and fired by electricity. Ranges of domestic ware, plus jugs and bowls for exhibition, are made, in addition to many commemorative pieces, mainly plates. Founder member of the Makers Guild in Wales.

Louise Darby

Louise Darby Born 1957. Studied three dimensional design, specializing in ceramics at Loughborough 1975-78. Worked at Torquil Pottery, Henley-in-Arden 1978-83. Taught part-time ceramics 1981-90. 1984 set up own workshop in converted pigsty near Stratford-on-Avon. Works alone making finely thrown stoneware and porcelain ceramic pieces, often involving additional building and/or incising. Details and tactile qualities are as important as the form, line and texture created. Uses various clay mixtures with own glazes and fires in a ceramic fibre gas kiln to 1280°C. Louise exhibits and sells widely in Britain.

Nick Douglas

Nick Douglas studied at Plymouth College of Art and Design. He first worked as resident potter at Bickleigh Mill Craft Centre near Tiverton in Devon, then with John Stuart in Exeter and later at West Pottery and in his own workshop in Ivybridge. Nick spent two years (1987-1988) in Nigeria based at the Minna Ceramics Centre, where he encouraged trainees towards self-supporting pottery production of domestic stoneware fired in wood and gas fired kilns. During his service, Nick secured a grant from the Canadian Development Commission to build and equip a studio pottery, which now runs successfully under the direction of Danlami Aliyu, a gifted Nigerian potter. Only two small gas injectors to fire the stoneware kiln needed to be imported. All the equipment, including two treadle operated kick wheels, raw material screens and the kiln were built by Danlami Aliyu.

Nick returned to Devon and has now re-established his pottery, producing a range of domestic stoneware and some one-off pieces. Although his work may not appear to be influenced by his experience in Nigeria, he does claim to be producing pots with maturity of form not previously evident. His use of a kick wheel similar in design to those in Nigeria, and the use of ash in most of his glazes have had their effect.

Bridget Drakeford

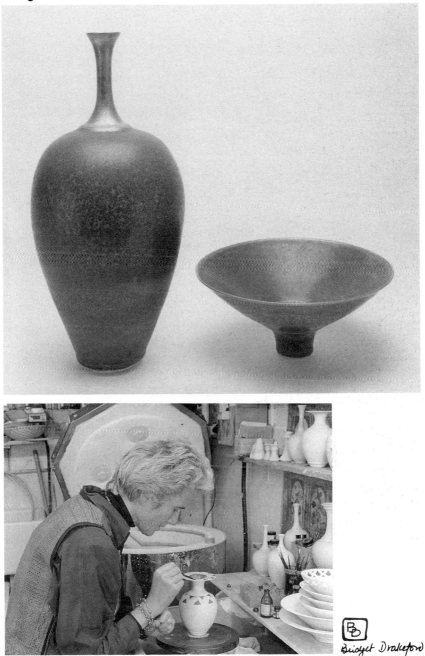

Bridget Drakeford

Bridget Drakeford Works alone making individual thrown porcelain. Simple classical shapes glazed with a copper crackle glaze or a matt white glaze decorated with coloured and gold on-glaze lustres. First workshop set up in South West Scotland in 1977 and moved to Worcestershire in 1983. Has exhibited widely in the U.K. and abroad.

Victoria and Michael Eden

EDEN

Victoria and Michael Eden 'Since 1981 we have worked together making slip-decorated domestic earthenware. We take the traditional slipware qualities of liveliness and humour as a starting point for our work, and to these we try to add something of ourselves and the time we live in. We have always enjoyed exploring the different qualities of slip, and now we are settled in our home and workshop we hope to experiment with firing techniques, particularly wood firing, and so bring new qualities to our work.'

Kirsti Buhler Fattorini

Kirsti Buhler Fattorini 'I was born in Switzerland being fortunate to be brought up in a community where the visual arts were highly regarded. On completing my formal education I went to Rome to study painting under Roberto Meli and ceramics under Salvator Meli. I made handbuilt earthenware pots decorated with bright abstract designs. On marrying and moving to England I was unable to find the materials I was used to and changed to stoneware thrown pots which I continue to decorate with abstract designs. More recently I have included slipcast stoneware dishes suitable for domestic use. I particularly enjoy decorating and experimenting with glazes. Currently my designs are drawn from nature — animals, birds, fish and flowers. My studio is a converted shed in the garden.'

Judith Fisher

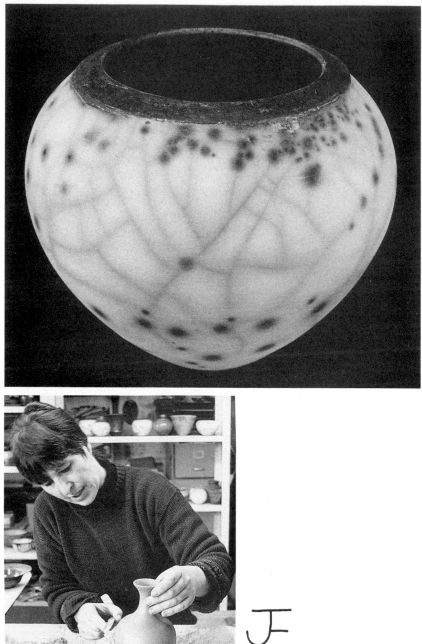

Judith Fisher Individual small-scale thrown porcelain bowls and vases fired by the raku method, in which the pot is withdrawn from a red-hot kiln and plunged into sawdust. When the piece is coated with a copper glaze before firing this can result in a range of lustrous colours from turquoise to bronze or, when it has received a special peel-away coating beforehand, an unglazed surface with marks and veining from the smoking process.

Alan Gaff

Alan Gaff Worked with Joe Finch at Appin Pottery 1979-87. Elected Fellow SPA 1983. Set up own workshop and showroom at Barcaldine by Loch Creran 1988. Produces hand thrown, mainly domestic stoneware pots which are hand painted, raw glazed and once-fired in a 65 cu.ft. down-draught wood kiln to 1300°C. 'We make a range of glazed ware for the kiln which are placed in the middle of the stack, and unglazed ware for the edge, where they get most effect from the wood ash. We enjoy making useful pots which people find pleasing to look at and can use in their everyday lives.'

Liz Gale

Liz Gale After training as a teacher, specializing in Textile Arts, Liz Gale taught in infant schools for ten years. Self-taught as a potter, she divided her time between teaching and ceramics, becoming a fulltime potter in 1988 and moving to her first purpose-built workshop and showroom in 1992. Specialising mainly in domestic reduction stoneware, she uses combination of latex, sponging, trailing and wax resist, to create decorations reminiscent of textile designs. She has just constructed a 30 cubic feet dry-built, gas-fired kiln. Since 1988 she has been involved in promoting the activities of Professional and Associate Members of the Craft Potters Association. Accepts commissions for full dinner services and individual decorative pieces.

Philip Gardiner

PG

Philip Gardiner 'After my initial training at North Staffordshire Polytechnic I worked at several small potteries, including eight years as a production thrower, before setting up my own pottery in 1983. The bulk of my production at present is low-fired stoneware, with a white zircon glaze and a range of pastel colours, in a wide range of shapes too many to list here. All my work is thrown and twice fired in an electric kiln. Many pieces are incised and/or decorated with 'clay flowers'.'

Rodney George

 AND

Rodney George started pottery in 1988 by attending evening classes at the Caversham Adult Education Centre in Reading. He has a small studio in his garden. He prefers making large thrown items, and also is keen on slab forming. He works only with earthenware clays, as he specialises in underglaze decoration, and sprigging. He uses three clays — a red terracotta, a buff 'school' clay, and a white china. He decorates with flowers, birds, animals, fruit, some abstract themes and scenery. He makes mugs, jugs, jars, platters, and perhaps specialises in cheese boards.

Graham Glynn

 G Ꮆ

Graham Glynn Studied at Oldham and Rochdale Schools of Art and at Wolverhampton Polytechnic. In 1981 after five years teaching, started workshop in Skipton selling most of work direct to public. Set up present workshop in 1988 selling to galleries and craft shops. Works alone. 'I work with oxidised stoneware fired with propane to 1280°C. In my thrown pottery I try to contrast quite precise shapes against loosely poured glazes. I also make coiled figures varying from 25cm to lifesize. Mostly silly old men with added birds and reptiles or anthropoid animals.'

Paul Green

Paul Green established his present workshop, Abbey Pottery in Cerne Abbas, Dorset in 1986. He is largely self-taught, but completed a workshop training course at Chester School of Art after following a career in historic building construction. He set up his first workshop in Wensleydale in the Yorkshire Dales, which he ran for six years. Abbey Pottery is a small country workshop producing a wide range of oven and tableware together with some more decorative porcelain. Most of the work is wheel-thrown and fired in a propane gas kiln to 1280°C in a reducing atmosphere. Glazes used are mainly ash, tenmoku, celadon and Kaki. The village of Cerne Abbas lies in beautiful countryside 8 miles north of Dorchester, the county town of Dorset. There is a well-stocked showroom at the pottery which is open throughout the year and is situated close to the famous Cerne Giant, a chalk figure carved into the nearby hillside.

Dimitra Grivellis

Dimitra Grivellis studied ceramics at Hammersmith School of Art and then gained wide experience as a production thrower at established potteries. Since '84 Dimitra has been working exclusively in porcelain, producing individual pieces, developing and using sandblasting techniques to decorate them. Her work consists of bowls, vases and plates. All are thrown using David Leach porcelain and oxidised to 1230/60C. Each piece is sandblasted, using a variety of resist masking materials, and colourfully decorated, mainly in relief. The decoration is inspired by wild animals and their habitats combined with traditional patterns from the relevant local culture. It is this combination that she loves, the beauty of porcelain, the controlled power of sandblasting, the joy of colour and a theme full of creative possibilities.

Frauke Güntzel

Frauke Güntzel 'I was born in Trier, Germany in 1963. Apprenticeship 1983-85 in Luxembourg. Worked afterwards in various workshops in Germany. Started studies in ceramics 1987 in Höhr-Grenzhausen, Germany, transferred to West Surrey College of Art and Design in Farnham after an exchange. Finished course in 1991 and worked for a few months in 401½ Wandsworth Road, London. Got setting-up grant from the Crafts Council in the same year and set up my own workshop at the beginning of 1992 in a garden centre near Farnham. I work with red earthenware clay, slips and transparent glazes and fire in an electric kiln. My work is sometimes handbuilt, sometimes thrown, often burnished. It is based on traditional subjects like the pouring vessel or goblet but it is only semi-functional. I produce a small range of domestic ware in order to survive. No sophisticated potter's mark, I only scratch my initials on the bottom.'

Morgen Hall

Morgen Hall 'I worked for Portsoy Pottery before attending Gray's School of Art in Aberdeen and then Cardiff Art College, working for Crathes and Appin Potteries in the summers. After teaching for a year I set up my present workshop at Chapter Arts Centre, Cardiff in 1986. I make wheel thrown and turned domestic tableware which, though highly decorated, is intended for everyday use. It is made from tin-glazed red earthenware, decorated with blue slip and mustard yellow stain. I also make a press moulded range with low relief decoration called 'Mardubi Ware'.'

Janet Halligan

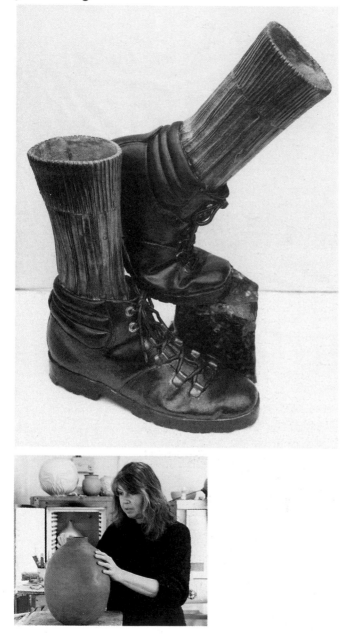

Janet Halligan graduated from Stourbridge College of Art in 1970. She lived and worked on the south coast until 1984, when she set up a workshop near Nantwich. Until recently she was known for 'trompe l'oeil' type work — that is everyday objects like shoes, bags, coats, food, made in clay and glazed to look realistic. She works mainly in stoneware. In the last year she has started to make sculptural pots and teapots derived from machine forms or natural forms. Work is handbuilt and consists mainly of one-off pieces. It is signed JH in iron oxide.

Michael and Barbara Hawkins

Michael and Barbara Hawkins Trained in Cornwall and Bristol. Established present workshop in Gloucestershire in 1979 with Craft Council grant. The pottery is highly decorated stoneware and porcelain, with use of lustres on the more one-off pieces. Range includes bottles, vases, bowls etc. with subjects such as fish, swans and flowers. The pots are fired in 90 cu.ft. catenary arch kiln (natural gas) designed and built by Wally Keeler (with help in its construction). Gloss firing to 1280°C, lustre firing to 760°C. Work is sold in galleries throughout the U.K. with some exported to Germany, Sweden and U.S.A.

Christopher Helson

Christopher Helson Born Caracas Venezuela 1965. 'I have lived and worked in Australia, Peru, Zimbabwe, U.S.A., Switzerland and Britain. I studied Ceramics at Manchester Polytechnic. My work is sculptural, predominantly wheel thrown and often therefore utilitarian. (These terms catagorize and therefore segregate, I find no differentia, simply an unhappy branding.) My recent pieces have been an exploration of reality, (earth and chaos, an interminable single breath and anarchy) when it is observed by an obliged western eye attached to a contingent physical body. Primarily concerning layers of conscious/unconscious physical glimpse/blind gaze and beauty. The work has minimal pre-applied glaze, I enjoy the continuity between clay and glaze created by fly ash in a cross-draught wood fired kiln. Firing to cone 11/12 and cooling slowly I have recently begun to explore cryptocrystallization of my 'high free silica' clay body and slips.'

Terri Holman

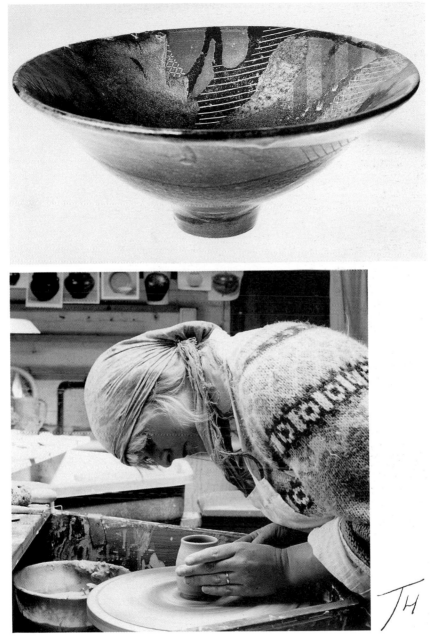

Terri Holman 'On leaving Cardiff in 1981, after three years at South Glamorgan Institute, I moved to Exeter where a group of artists joined forces to open a deserted railway warehouse as studios. At this time I became a member of the Devon Guild of Craftsmen. A move to Torquay enabled me to open my present workshop. The work has developed in two directions over this ten-year period. The smaller porcelain bowls and lidded boxes of intricate enamel decoration contrasts with the larger stoneware bowls and vases where the glazes, enamels and lustres are used more freely.'

Ashley Howard

Ashley Howard was born in Kent in 1963. After school he worked in a local graphics studio before studying ceramics at Medway College of Art and Design 1983-87. As a student he worked for potters John Pollex in Plymouth and Mike Goddard in the Dordogne. He also travelled to Northern India. He works for galleries and exhibitions using thrown, altered and handbuilt techniques at stoneware and earthenware temperatures. He uses a distinctive purple/blue dry glaze and a pale glaze with coloured slip decoration.

Eileen Jones

Eileen Jones 'I began potting in 1981, 32 years after a brief introduction to pottery at Goldsmiths' College during my training as an arts and crafts teacher 1945-48. I owe much to David and Margaret Frith whose excellent summer schools I enjoyed and gained from for five years and to many potters whose day seminars I attended at every possible occasion. My present work falls into two categories. I make domestic stoneware, jugs, bowls, platters, mugs, teapots etc. using a variety of glazes, including ash glazes, decorating with wax relief or overlapped glazes or just occasionally brushwork. I also work in porcelain, making one-off pieces: bowls, lidded boxes, bottle-vases, teapots, all carved and/or fluted and glazed with delicate celadon-like glazes. Most of the work I make is thrown, though some of the domestic ware is made over the hump moulds or slabbed. The stoneware and porcelain pieces are fired together in an electric kiln to Orton Cone 9. We are in the process of selling this house with its very small workshop, so that I can have bigger premises with retail outlet. Change of address will be advertised in *Ceramic Review*.'

Vresh David Kanikanian

Vresh David Kanikanian 'I studied fine art in Baghdad then joined Chelsea School of Art for four years and obtained my diploma in painting special level. I then joined the pottery and sculpture department at Ealing College. The clay and glazes fascinated me and I involved myself more and more in making functional pots, also as part of compositions. As an Armenian born in Iraq, the blue green glaze influences me which I use on most of my pots especially on double skin vases on which I cut out Arabic calligraphy on outer skin. I also use the shape of the cross in most of my sculptural pieces. At present I teach part-time at the Polytechnic of West London and look after my studio and gallery in Ealing.

Jonathan Keep

Jonathan Keep Born in 1958. Studied Natal University, South Africa. Moved to the U.K. in 1986 and set up a studio in Snape Maltings, Suffolk. Recently moved to nearby Knodishall where I have a studio and showroom. 'I make a wide range of pots, a standard range of kitchen and tableware, individually decorated domestic ware and large sculptural pots. Working by myself I aim to produce pots that are well crafted, well-designed and pleasing to live with. Most work is thrown in a semi-porcelain white clay or a red clay and decorated with coloured slips. I fire to a low stoneware temperature (1220°C), in an electric kiln.'

Julian King-Salter

Julian King-Salter Born 1954. Set up as full-time potter in 1983. Self taught. Makes individual handbuilt stoneware pots using flattened coils followed by pinching and stroking, without scraping. Own recipe glazes are applied to biscuited ware by pouring and brushing, with up to three layers, and fired to cone 9 in an electric kiln. Solo exhibitions with Leigh Gallery, London; Royal Exchange, Manchester; Peter Dingley, Stratford; Beaux Arts, Bath; Scottish Gallery, Edinburgh; and New Ashgate Gallery, Farnham. Work regularly supplied to these and other galleries around the country.

Kirton Pottery

Kirton Pottery The pottery was set up in 1974 by Peter and Christine Hawes when they returned to England from Botswana where they started a pottery training workshop. Peter is self-taught while Christine studied pottery before specializing in painting at Sheffield College of Art. The pottey at first made traditional slipware but now concentrates on stoneware and majolica, mainly domestic ware but also a fair number of sculptural pieces. We work as a team, the throwing being done by Peter and our full-time assistant Lea Cox. Lea Bason decorates part-time in her own style. We all make individual sculptural work.

Gaynor Lindsell

Gaynor Lindsell After several years as head of art in a London comprehensive school, studied and taught ceramics in New York. She set up her own studio on returning to England in 1988 and also worked as an assistant to Colin Pearson. Her work explores flow and movement in the form and seeks to integrate form, surface colour and texture. Her pots are thrown, ribbed and altered. She currently works in low-fired clays and uses the ancient Greek technique of terra sigillata to produce a subtle surface sheen which is enhanced by burnishing. She enjoys giving workshops and has exhibited in England and the U.S.A.

Christine McCole

LLANBOIDY

Christine McCole Trained at Harrow, studio pottery course 1977-1979. Together with her partner Roger Brann, set up the pottery in Llanboidy in 1980. Makes raw glazed domestic ware, woodfired to 1280°C in a 40 cu.ft. fast-fire kiln. Member of the Makers Guild in Wales. Pots sold mainly from the workshop.

Vinitha McWhinnie

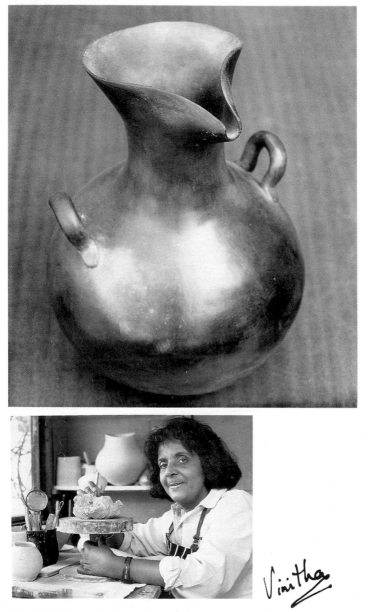

Vinitha McWhinne's present collection of ceramics consists of large to small vessel forms, hand-built or sometimes thrown and altered; terrasigillata is applied, burnished and lustred. Decoration is a reduction firing in her garden using sawdust. Porcelain, stoneware and terracotta are used. Vinitha read Natural Science in Sri Lanka where her involvement in ceramics started and it continued in London. After a diploma and post-diploma period in the Midlands she set up a studio in Solihull, working on large sculptural forms in oxidised stoneware. Vinitha has travelled extensively, observing pottery in France, Germany, Greece, Yugoslavia, India and Japan, but the burnished pots of the Pueblo Indians in Arizona and her own origins have influenced her current work. She conducts workshops and demonstrations and in 1990-92 has exhibited at the Crafts Council of Great Britain, at Bonham's in London, and also at museums and galleries in the Midlands and north of Britain.

Made in Cley

MADE IN
CLEY

Made in Cley is a crafts cooperative established in 1981 comprising five potters and a jeweller: Wolf Altmann, Gunhild Espelage, Richard Kelham, Rosalind Redfern, Barbara Widdup, and Quay Proctor-Mears (the jeweller). 'We produce a very wide range of wheel-thrown, reduction and oxidized-fired stoneware for domestic use and also individual and sculptural pieces in stoneware and porcelain. Since 1984 our work is sold through our Gallery situated in a beautiful village on the North Norfolk coast, in an old Georgian shop that in itself is of historic interest.'

Fenella Mallalieu

Fenella Mallalieu 'My intention as a potter is to make functional pots for special occasions — pots to give eating a sense of ceremony. I readily admit to a love of throwing and I aim to interfere with that at little as possible by keeping turning to a minimum. I am drawn to particular forms — fat bellied jugs, wide bowls, wide rimmed plates and ovals. The latter made by picking up a soft round disc and chucking it across my work table. I mark out my pattern with terracotta slip and then paint and wax those areas before dipping in the background glaze. I work in white earthenware, bisque fired to 1160°C, and have half a dozen glazes which are all food safe.'

Angela Mellor

Angela Mellor was born in Cheshire. Trained as a teacher gaining Distinction in Art and Design 1968. Took an Advanced Certificate in Art Education, specialising in Ceramics, studying under Peter Lane, at the University of East Anglia 1984. Built a studio at home in Grantchester in 1991. Works mainly in porcelain making individual slab-built pieces, with impressed decoration. This is enhanced by painting and spraying underglaze colours. Her work is inspired by natural forms, notably plant and marine life. Angela has exhibited widely in this country, also in America, France and Germany.

Kate Mellors

Kate Mellors 'I trained at Camberwell School of Art from 1972-75 and on leaving shared a workshop in Greenwich, London and taught part-time in Adult Education. I made a range of tableware and also individual thrown and decorated pieces. In 1980 I set up a workshop at home. In about 1985 I started making stoneware garden pottery. This new direction arose from my interest in gardens, traditional architecture and garden pottery. Travel in the Far East in 1986 provided further inspiration. In 1990 I moved to West Dorset and gave up teaching. I now work full-time making a range of garden lanterns, bird-baths, planters, tables and stools. These are all ash-glazed and once-fired in an electric kiln.'

Toff Milway

Toff Milway Saltglaze country potter, producing a variety of domestic kitchenware and individual dinner services in saltglaze. Some large decorative pieces. Introduced to saltglaze working with Gwyn Hanssen in France. Extended periods abroad working in Africa and USA. 'I now live and work in the beautiful Cotswold village of Conderton, and sell all I make from my own studio gallery. Commissions undertaken. Occasional exhibitions. Committee member of the Gloucestershire Guild of Craftsmen.'

Jill Moger

Jill Moger Her work falls into two distinct categories, wildlife studies which predominate, and humorous/satirical subjects. A love of wildlife, particularly reptiles and birds, has led her to concentrate her ceramics in this field. She endeavours to bring out the very best in her subjects by exaggerating their finer points, thus making each original sculpture unmistakably her own. Intricate details are finely modelled to give a strong sense of realism. Handbuilt sculptures in porcelain or stoneware. Fired to 1260°C in an electric kiln. Various, glazes, stains and lustres. Work widely represented in Britain and abroad. Regular exhibitions.

Roger Mulley

Roger Mulley specialises in large hand thrown pots which he decorates in a variety of slips and glazes. He especially enjoys throwing 'large ware', many of his pots being 50 or 60 kg in weight. Most of his work is decorated with paper resist and sgraffito designs using coloured slips. Some pots are raw glazed while others are left unglazed to leave a natural matt finish. His range includes both earthenware and stoneware. Roger Mulley makes many individual pieces for private commissions. Work also includes large conservatory glazed planters and decorated garden terracotta. His pots are mainly sold from his workshop at Clanfield Pottery, which he and his wife, Sarah, established 16 years ago. Roger Mulley's work is now found in many private collections both in the U.K. and abroad.

Sue Munday

Sue Munday specialised in ceramics at North Staffordshire Polytechnic, graduating in 1986. 'Since then I have established my workshop where I create tactile forms by throwing and hand-building. This allows me greater freedom to alter the rhythm and direction of each piece. 'T' material and White Stoneware are used together to build each form which are then textured, using metal and wooden tools, these are enriched by the use of slips and latex. With an open clay body and a reduction firing the vanadium stained glaze inside the form permeates through to the outer surfaces, giving colour without glazing.

Stephen Murfitt

SM
STEPHEN MURFITT
CERAMICS

Stephen Murfitt Groups of four to six similar forms are built at the same time by a combination of throwing and coiling techniques. The work is bisque fired in an electric kiln to 1000°C and then glazed using a range of glazes based on alkaline and borax frits with additional oxides. A variety of colours and lustrous effects are achieved by the subsequent raku process, which involves firing the pots in a ceramic fibre kiln, followed by reduction in bins of sawdust. Has exhibited widely and is represented in numerous private and public collections.

Tessa Wolfe Murray

Tessa Wolfe Murray Trained in Ceramics at Goldsmiths' College, 1982-84. Vases and dishes are slab-built, and candlesticks slip-cast in red earthenware. They are decorated with slips, stains and glazes and fired twice in an electric kiln. The final low temperature smoking is achieved in an open sawdust kiln. Flat shapes with a soft elliptical curve, almost like cardboard cut-outs when seen from a distance, are contradicted by the illusory depths of the surface decoration which suggest ocean depths or cloud-strewn skies. Exhibits and sells to galleries in the U.K., Germany and Holland.

Christine Niblett

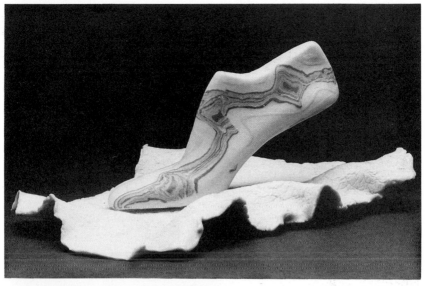

Christine Niblett Born in Cheshire in 1935, she moved to Palma de Mallorca, Spain in 1966, where she now lives. Initial studies included 4 years at the Palma School of Applied Arts (Ceramics). She now works solely in laminated porcelain, body-stained with natural metal oxides, reduction-fired to 1260°C, mainly unglazed. Her Mediterranean surroundings have influenced the flowing patterns integrated into her fragile, undulating forms. Her location allows her to participate in exhibitions, courses and competitions throughout Europe, including Arte-Fiera, Bologna; Ob'Art, Paris; Siklos International Ceramics Symposium, Hungary (1989); International Biennial of Ceramic Art, Vallauris (1988, 1990, 1992).

Jacqueline Norris

Jacqueline Norris is a designer and maker of decorative ceramics which reflect an indulgence in colour and texture. Her training came from the Harrow Studio Pottery course followed by a Masters at The Royal College of Art. She uses a clay mixture of T-material and porcelain which offers a perfect surface and whiteness to enhance applied textures and rich glazes. Most of Jacqueline's current ceramics are slab built although she has recently reintroduced throwing into her work. Her kiln is a small electric Cromartie which she regularly fires to 1260°C allowing a quick succession of results. Glazes are applied liberally by brush. Jacqueline's studio is a converted cow shed, part of a former convent on the edge of Burnham Beeches, South Buckinghamshire.

Carol Peever

Carol Peever
1992

or

Carol Peever
The year

Carol Peever 'I was born in 1953 at Ironbridge in Shropshire. I studied ceramics at Wolverhampton Polytechnic from 1976 to 1979. I now live and work in Wednesbury in the West Midlands. My working space is small and luckily so are my pots. I make a range of one-off forms which are built in press moulds, this limits the shape, but I feel happy with the fact as there seems to be no limit to ideas I have for pattern and additions to the forms. So far I make bowls, basket forms, lidded jars, spoons and sets of cup/plate/saucer/spoon. I use semi-porcelain clay, bisque to 1000°C, sand the insides, decorate with colourful underglazes and refire to 1250°C. The work is for sale through galleries.'

Nancy Pickard

Nancy Pickard Born in 1963 in Sao Paulo, Brazil. 'I spent my teenage years in the Channel Islands before attending what was then the Central School of Art, and the Cardiff Institute. Now I make handbuilt pots for exhibition all over the country. Like a thrower, I enjoy the handling of raw clay, with a minimum of complicated equipment, and I am striving for the same freshness of form and surface that a practised thrower achieves. I use an ordinary rolling pin to make slabs, which are then textured, cut up and assembled. The glazes, at the moment are in a range of pinks, terracotta, mauve and purple, with flashes of other colours in the surface. The ware is not designed for the table, but I do like to see it displayed in the home, as it is full of domestic references. I make a range of forms; teapots, jugs, trays, bottles etc. Each piece is unique in detail. I seldom use a potter's mark as I feel that my marks are all over it in the vocabulary of the technique.'

Philomena Pretsell

Philomena Pretsell Edinburgh College of Art 1987-1989 (BA Hons) Diploma in Post Graduate Studies 1989-1990. 'Since the early 1970s I have been interested in maintaining the soft tactile quality of wet clay. Resembling fabric when decorated with coloured earthenware slips, the clay slabs are cut and folded into vessel forms. The work is mostly non-functional, but based on familiar domestic items, teapots, jugs etc. The functional work includes candleholders, fruit baskets, plant stands, napkin rings etc.' Various open weekends throughout the year. Work available at galleries including London, Oxford, Leeds and Edinburgh.

Ursula Morley Price

Ursula Morley Price Studied painting at Camberwell and the Slade School. In 1972 returned to S.W. France and set up studio, lived and worked in France for 15 years, broken only by two short periods of working in Essex. In 1985 spent two years in New Zealand teaching and working in her studio in Auckland. Returned to U.K. in 1987 and set up her present studio in Brighton, Sussex. Makes handbuilt stoneware and porcelain forms influenced by Japanese paper decorations; engineers clay and builds it seemingly to its limits. 1981 British Council Award. 1984 Artist in Residence at the Studio Experimental Sèvres Paris. Member of Maison de Metiers D'Art Francais. Slide Index of Musee des Arts Decoratifs, Paris. Slide Index South East Arts. Exhibited widely in Europe, New Zealand and U.S.A. Work in many public and private collections throughout Europe and U.S.A. Ursula does regular workshops and slide talks in Europe and U.S.A.

Audrey Richardson Trained originally in painting and sculpture at Duncan of Jordanstone College of Art, Dundee, Scotland. Started potting through attending local evening classes. Works alone, making individual pots and sculptures. These are handbuilt, using mainly T material, then decorated with a selected range of slips and glazes. The work is fired to 1250°C. Also makes some large garden sculptures; and will undertake portraits on commission. Present workshop is in an idyllic situation, overlooking the River Wey. Showcase of current work on display.

Michael and Wendy Salt

Michael and Wendy Salt 'We have been studio potters at Aislaby, North Yorkshire for 12 years. We work in stoneware, porcelain and terracotta making a range of pots for use in home and garden, and a variety of individual items. The versatility of working methods and materials enables us to play and experiment rather than standardise. We feel the particularness of a pot's making (the frozen moment) gives so much more to contemplate than just a technical solution to a functional problem, or the declaration of an idea, important as these might be.'

Caroline Seaton

Caroline Seaton lives and works in an attractive small village with thatched cottages and a castle. Her pottery is in the old chapel, with the light, airy Sunday School room used as the show room. Caroline likes making individual pots to complement food. She uses most hand made methods, with her large thrown bowls being a best seller. Both terra-cotta and stoneware clays are used with a lovely deep blue dappled glaze for the terra-cotta and soft sugared almond colours on the stoneware.

Sheila Seepersaud-Jones

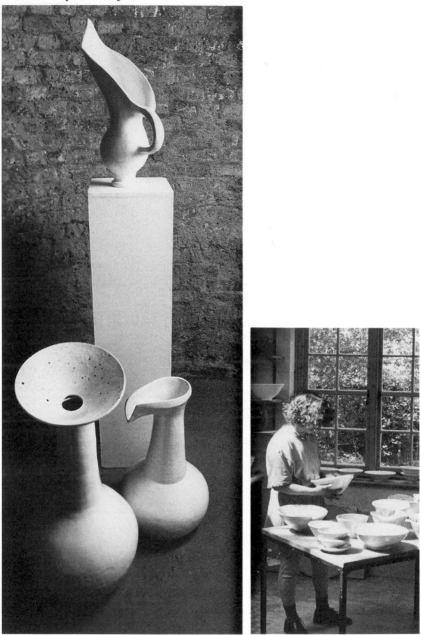

Sheila Seepersaud-Jones Born in Guyana. 'I taught English before coming to England to train as a nurse. Later I developed my interest in art and achieved a BA Hons in Fine Art, St. Martins School of Art, London. As initially I was concerned with exploration of three dimensional forms I chose to do my degree in sculpture. Latterly I have concentrated on clay to explore texture, colour and pattern on three dimensional surfaces. Work is both sculptural and traditional. I make coiled, slabbed and thrown pots fired at 1100°C-1250°C. I hand paint my pieces in designs which reflect my Caribbean and European backgrounds.

Ifigenija Simonović

Ifigenija Simonović I was born in 1953, Ljubljana, Slovenija, and came to live in England in 1978. I studied pottery at Harrow College and have been a full time potter since 1985, also teaching for the Adult Education, Epping Forest College. I specialize in making thrown and turned earthenware pots, mainly bowls and teapots. Nearly all my pots are glazed with tin glaze and painted in so called majolica way, directly on a glazed but not yet fired pot. I also paint bone china, which is slipcast in Stoke on Trent, many limited editions made in moulds after my own original models. My side lines are slab-built serving dishes, painted tiles, miniature pots, jewellery and sculpture.

Peter Sparrey

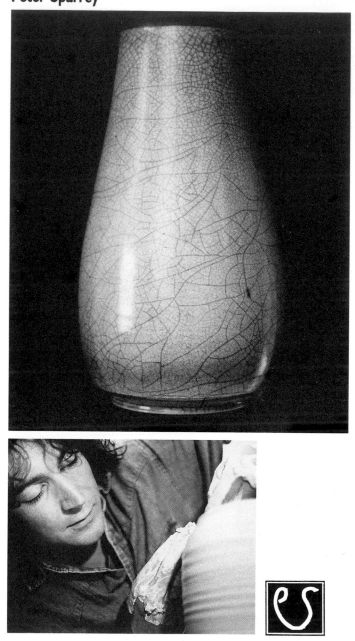

Peter Sparrey 'After training at the Guernsey Pottery C.I. I returned to England to set up a pottery in Malvern. I now concentrate purely on thrown raku ceramics. I use either pocelain or white stoneware clay bodies to produce mainly vases and dishes, fired in a gas kiln to 1000°C. The white, blues, greens, turquoise and rich lustres of my pots are achieved from combinations of metal oxides in the glaze, these being copper, cobalt, chrome and tin. I sell throughout the U.K. in gallery outlets and direct from my workshop in Malvern.'

Chris Speyer

Chris Speyer Trained as a theatre designer and worked in theatre for many years. Now, as the ceramic half of Yerja Ceramics & Textiles, makes thrown and press moulded stoneware. Work exhibited and sold throughout the U.K. and abroad.

Christel Spriet

Christel Spriet studied ceramics at the Saint-Lucas Instituut for Fine Art in Belgium, graduating in 1986. During her college education she specialized in the design of glazes, throwing and sculptural form. After graduating she moved to England and her studio is currently in Framingham, Suffolk. After making sculptural pots in stoneware and porcelain for a few years she is now making wall-sculptures. Moving to a larger two-dimensional surface allows her more scope for expression. She uses T-material and different layers of slips, oxides and glazes to achieve the finished result. The sculptures start as one piece of clay which is textured then cut into tiles for firing. The finished tiles are mounted to form the final sculpture.

Rebecca Taylor

Rebecca Taylor Her pots are generally unglazed, heavily textured and oxided in either earthy and mossy colours or metallic and spangled hues, thus giving respectively an ancient or medieval appearance. Using unusual methods she obtains unorthodox finishes sometimes firing straight to stone to retain colour and 'feel'. Her latticed pieces bring a new dimension to potting with an almost metallic ring to them. Her experiments with life forms and strange textures have created a new look which is both functional and sculptural which have made her popular in both Spain and Greece.

Lyndon Thomas

Lyndon Thomas Born 1941, I have received no formal training in pottery, the skills being accumulated by means of voracious reading and endless practice. In 1967 I set up my first workshop and supply work to various craft outlets. All work is thrown with functional shapes predominating; I obtain greatest satisfaction from making jugs, storage jars and shallow bowls. The bulk of production is oxidised stoneware fired to a maximum temperature of 1270°C in a 12 cubic ft. electric kiln. The clay is grogged stoneware produced by Spencroft, suitable for large and small scale work. Glazes are developed from various recipes with iron being the main colourant.

Katrina Trinick

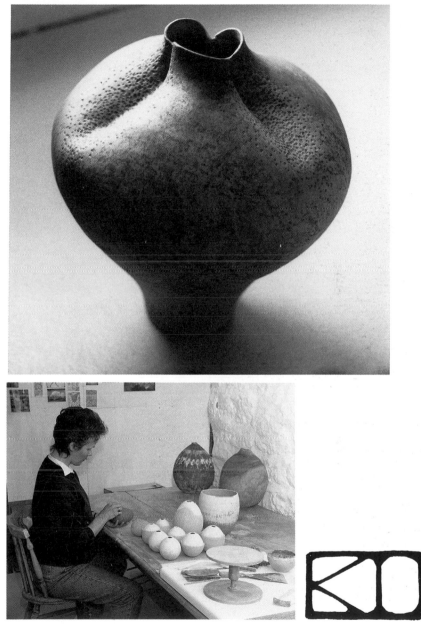

Katrina Trinick Born in Cornwall in 1950. Dip A.D. Ceramics at Central School of Art and Design 1969-72. 'My present workshop was set up in 1991, where I work alone. All work is hand-built, coiled and pinched, and varies from small to quite large (25" tall). Individual non-domestic pots fired to 1250°C. I live close to a granite tor with massive weathered boulders, bearing various lichens: I draw ideas for form and surface from these and from shells and pebbles found on the beach. I am also interested in Celtic and earlier carvings found on granite.' Work sold through Cornwall Craft Association Galleries and the Chapel Gallery, Saltram near Plymouth.

Clare Parsons Trucco

Clare Parsons Trucco specializes in domestic stoneware pottery that can be used and enjoyed every day. Functionality is coupled with hand carved decoration inspired by wood carving designs and the smooth fluid shapes of pre-Columbian pottery. In addition to her own designs, she enjoys realising pots for specific projects through discussions with customers. After training at Harrow, Clare was a resident potter at South Bank Craft Centre in London for two years. She then worked in Bogota, Colombia, for a local pottery and gathered material on pre-Columbian and contemporary forms and decoration. Clare is now based in Edinburgh.

Tydd Pottery

Tydd Pottery We make a range of hand-thrown, oil-fired, terracotta garden pots.

Sue Varley

SV

Sue Varley.

Sue Varley 'I studied at the Bath Academy of Art, where I specialised in ceramics and was taught by James Tower. I make both earthenware and stoneware pots. Some of my ideas for form and decoration come from looking at landscape, rock formation, strata, etc. The colours found in stones and pebbles are often a starting point for clays and glazes — I mix oxides and/or grog into the basic clay body. The earthenware pots are first fired in an electric kiln and then smoked in sawdust, newspaper or grasses. I uses mixed woodash glazes for my stoneware pots and fire to 1250°C in an electric kiln.'

Carol Wainwright

Carol Wainwright trained as a painter at Harrow School of Art in the late fifties and two decades later in ceramics at West Surrey. While still a student at W.S.C.A.D. she established her home workshop and built a gas kiln. Clay she buys "as dug" from Dorset where she weathers, soaks and pugs it. She has concentrated on making bowls and plates which provide suitable surfaces for vigorously brushed decoration built from multiple layers of coloured glazes. Variety of form, surface and colour are important. She also makes larger ware, providing sizeable canvases for free brushwork.

Nicola Werner

Nicola Werner 'I make my living throwing pots in Fremington red earthenware, dipping them in tin glaze and decorating the white surfaces with colourful brushwork birds, flowers and lambs in the majolica tradition. It is basically a simple approach and a reaction to my original ideals when studying Fine Art at Central School of Art and Design. I love the painting but particularly balanced with the manual vigour of throwing and all the other myriad sides of running a business. It is this combination of the visually pleasing and the practical which really appeals. I trained at Aldermaston pottery 1982-5 and set up on my own in 1986. My aim is to make useful pots and tiles to enhance everyday life. The work is available direct, by appointment, or at selected galleries including the Victoria and Albert Museum Shop.'

George Wilson

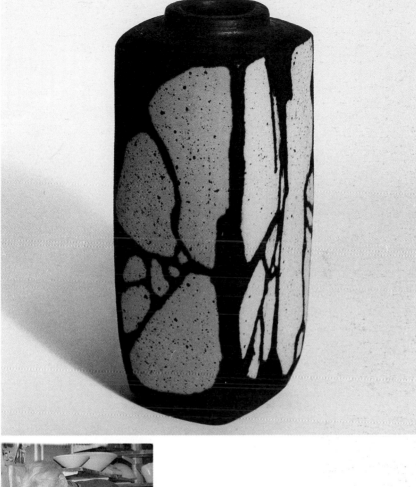

George Wilson

George Wilson took early retirement from full-time teaching at the Richmond Adult College (where he was the founder of the Ceramics Department) in order to devote more time to producing his own work in his Ealing, West London studio. He continues to teach part-time at Brunel University and Surbiton College. He works mainly in reduction and oxidised stoneware and in lustred porcelain, producing individual decorative pieces for interior designers and architects, and containers for Ikebana flower arranging. George exhibits widely in the U.K. and sells work in America and Europe. He aims to have at least one major solus exhibition a year. He is currently designing and producing a range of pottery exclusive to leading London stores.

Gill Wright

Gill Wright works in red earthenware and makes handbuilt pots which are burnished and sawdust fired.

Visiting a Potter

This is a full list of names and addresses of Fellows and Professional members of the CPA, together with details of opening hours. The map gives approximate geographical position. Map numbers correspond to those following the potters' names and addresses.

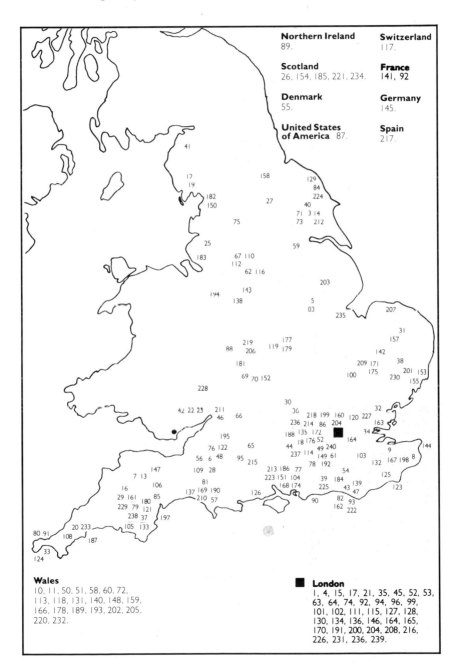

Northern Ireland	Switzerland
89.	117.

Scotland	France
26, 154, 185, 221, 234.	141, 92

Denmark	Germany
55.	145.

| United States of America 87. | Spain 217. |

Wales
10, 11, 50, 51, 58, 60, 72, 113, 118, 131, 140, 148, 159, 166, 178, 189, 193, 202, 205, 220, 232.

■ **London**
1, 4, 15, 17, 21, 35, 45, 52, 53, 63, 64, 74, 92, 94, 96, 99, 101, 102, 111, 115, 127, 128, 130, 134, 136, 146, 164, 165, 170, 191, 200, 204, 208, 216, 226, 231, 236, 239.

Addresses of Fellows

Adrian Abberley   1
95a Sheen Road
Richmond-upon-Thames
Surrey

081-948 1234

Please telephone

Tim Andrews   2
Lowerdown Pottery
Bovey Tracey
Devon
TQ13 9LE

0626 833076

Mick Arnup   3
Holtby Pottery
Holtby
York YO1 3UA

York (0904) 489377

Showroom open 10.00 - 18.00 every day.
Holtby is five miles from York on A166

Keith Ashley   4
rear of 191 Archway Road
London N6 5BN

071-267 9032

Visitors welcome

Chris Aston   5
Chris Aston Pottery
Yew Tree Cottage
4 High Street
Elkesley
Nr Retford Notts
DN22 8AJ

Telephone and Fax 077 783 391

The village of Elkesley, once part of the lands
belonging to the Dukes of Portland and
Newcastle on the edge of Sherwood Forest, is
on the A1, 20 miles north of Newark, and
only 20 minutes drive from Rufford.

Visitors are always welcome in Chris'
workshop and gallery/showroom.

Open: generally 7 days a week 10 am to
6 pm.

Felicity Aylieff   6
19 Fairfield Park Road
Bath
BA1 6JW

0225 334136

Visitors welcome but by appointment only

Svend Bayer   7
Duckpool Cottage
Sheepwash
Beaworthy
Devon EX21 5PW

Black Torrington (040923) 282

Pottery always open. Visitors welcome but
best to telephone first

Michael Bayley   8
Beechcroft Cottage
Green Lane
Temple Ewell
Dover
Kent CT16 3AS

Dover (0304) 822624

Visitors are welcome. Please telephone for
directions

Peter Beard   9
The Pottery
Bottom Pond Road
Wormshill
nr Sittingbourne, Kent
ME9 0TR

Wormshill (062 784) 554

Studio open at any reasonable time.
Visitors are very welcome but must make an
appointment

Beverley Bell-Hughes   10
Fron Dirion
Conwy Road
Llandudno Junction
Gwynedd LL31 9AY

Aberconwy 0492 572575

Visitors by appointment only

Terry Bell-Hughes 11
Fron Dirion
Conwy Road
Llandudno Junction
Gwynedd, North Wales
LL31 9AY

Aberconwy (0492) 572575

Visitors by appointment only

Maggie Angus Berkowitz 12
21-23 Park Road
Milnthorpe
Cumbria LA7 7AD

05395 63970 (Tel)
05395 63487 (Fax)

Workshop at home; visitors by appointment

Clive Bowen 13
Shebbear Pottery
Shebbear, Beaworthy
Devon EX21 5QZ

Shebbear (0409) 281271

Wholesale and retail customers are welcome
at the showroom

Loretta Braganza 14
The Coach House
198 Mount Vale
York, Yorkshire YO2 2DL

York (0904) 630454

Visitors by appointment only

Carlo Briscoe and Edward Dunn 15
494 Archway Road
Highgate
London N6 4NA

Telephone and Fax 081-341 4908

Visitors welcome but by appointment only

Sandy Brown 16
38 East Street
South Molton
Devon EX36 3DF

South Molton (0769) 572829

Usually open; please telephone first

Ian Byers 17
10 Westbourne Road
Croydon
CR0 6HP

081-654 0225

Visitors are welcome by appointment

Alan Caiger-Smith 18
Aldermaston Pottery
Aldermaston
Reading
Berkshire RG7 4LW

(0734) 713359

Opening hours 8 am-5 pm, except Sundays

John Calver 19
23 Silverdale Road
Yealand Redmayne
Carnforth, Lancs.
LA5 9TA

(0524) 781362

Visitors are welcome to the workshop but
please telephone first

Seth Cardew 20
Wenford Bridge Pottery
St. Breward
Bodmin
Cornwall
PL30 3PN

Bodmin (0208) 850471

Visitors welcome by appointment

Daphne Carnegy 21
Kingsgate Workshops
110-116 Kingsgate Road
London NW6

071 328 2051

Visitors welcome by appointment

Michael Casson 22
Wobage Farm
Upton Bishop
Ross-on-Wye
Herefordshire HR9 7QP

Upton Bishop (098985) 233

Showroom open 10 am-5 pm on Saturdays
and Sundays. For other times please telephone
first

Sheila Casson 23
Wobage Farm
Upton Bishop
Ross-on-Wye
Herefordshire HR9 7QP

Upton Bishop (098985) 233

Showroom open 10 am-5 pm on Saturdays
and Sundays. For other times please telephone
first

249

Jenny Clarke 24
25 Eltoe Road
Westbury Park
Bristol
BS6 7NZ

Bristol (0272) 735193

Derek Clarkson 25
I The Poplars
Bacup
Lancashire OL13 8AD

Bacup (0706) 874541

Visitors welcome, telephone first is possible

Margery Clinton 26
The Pottery
Newton Port
Haddington
East Lothian

Haddington (062 082) 3584

The pottery and showroom are open daily
except Sunday and Monday, but visitors are
advised to telephone to confirm

Peter Clough 27
34 Dragon View
Harrogate
North Yorkshire
HG1 4DG

(0423) 506700 (Home)
(0765) 602691 (Work)

Visitors by prior arrangement only

Russell Coates 28
10 The Butts
Frome
Somerset
BA11 4AA

(0373) 452443

Visitors welcome but please telephone first

Roger Cockram 29
Chittlehampton Pottery
Victoria House
Chittlehampton
North Devon
EX37 9PX

(0769) 540420

Visitors welcome 9 am-6 pm weekdays. Usually
also weekends, but best telephone first

Russell Collins 30
Hook Norton Pottery
East End Farmhouse
Hook Norton
Banbury Oxon.
OX15 5LG

(0608) 737414 (Tel)
(0608) 730442 (Fax)

Showroom is open Mon-Sat 9.00 am-5.00 pm

Barbara Colls 31
177 Thunder Lane
Thorpe St Andrew
Norwich NR7 0JF

Norwich (0603) 36695

Visitors welcome by appointment

Joanna Constantinidis 32
2 Bells Chase
Great Baddow
Chelmsford
Essex CM2 8DT

(0245) 71842

Visitors by appointment

Delan Cookson 33
Lissadell
St Buryan
Penzance
Cornwall
TR19 6HP

(0736) 810347

Visitors welcome at showroom/workshop by
appointment

Bennett Cooper 34
Mistley Quay Workshops
Mistley
Manningtree
Essex CO11 1HB

(0206) 393884

Showroom open seven days a week 10.00
am-6.00 pm

Emmanuel Cooper 35
Fonthill Pottery
38 Chalcot Road
London NW1 8LP

071-722 9090

Visitors welcome by appointment

Gilles Le Corre 36
19 Howard Street
Oxford
OX4 3AY
Oxford (0865) 245289

Visitors by appointment

Dartington Pottery 37
Shinners Bridge
Dartington
Totnes
Devon TQ9 6JE
Totnes (0803) 864163

Shop opening hours Monday-Saturday
10.00 am-6.00 pm

Clive Davies 38
Valley Barn
Homersfield
Harleston
Norfolk IP20 0NS
Homersfield (098 686) 8144

Visit us, but check first we are around

Derek Davis 39
Duff House
Maltravers Street
Arundel
West Sussex BN18 9AP
Arundel (0903) 882600

Visitors by appointment

Peter and Jill Dick 40
Coxwold Pottery
Coxwold
York YO6 4AA
Coxwold (034 76) 344

Visitors are welcome to visit the pottery
showroom and see work in progress. Opening
times: Tuesday till Friday and Summer Sundays
2.00-5.00 pm. As there are normally only the
two of us it is wise to telephone before
making a special journey. Group visits by
appointment only.

Mike Dodd 41
'Wellrash'
Boltongate
nr Wigton, Cumbria
CA5 1DH
Low Ireby (09657) 615

Showroom open most of the time, but
advisable to ring first

Jack Doherty 42
Hooks Cottage
Lea Bailey
Ross-on-Wye
Herefordshire
HR9 5TY
Lea (0989) 750644

Visitors are welcome at the workshop &
showroom please telephone first

John Dunn 43
Open Studios
168 Kings Road Arches
Brighton, Sussex
(0273) 725013/822207

Visitors welcome by apointment

Geoffrey Eastop 44
The Pottery
Ecchinswell
near Newbury
Berkshire RG15 8TT
Kingsclere (0635) 298220

Open most days by appointment

Dorothy Feibleman 45
10 Arlingford Road
London SW2 2SU
081-674 8979

Visitors welcome by appointment

Ray Finch 46
Winchcombe Pottery
Broadway Road
Winchcombe
Cheltenham
Glos. GL54 5NU
Winchcombe (0242) 602462

Open all year Monday-Friday 9.00 am-5.00 pm
Saturday 10.00 am-4.00 pm (Showroom only)
May-September Sunday Noon-4.00 pm
(Showroom only)

Jutka Fischer 47
84 Chapel Street
Newhaven
East Sussex
BN9 9QD
0273 516131

Visitors welcome by appointment only

Robert Fournier   48
Ashley Groom
Ashley House
Box
Wiltshire SN14 9AN

Box (0225) 742416

Fournier Pottery, **Robert Fournier** entered
the Central School of Arts and Crafts 1945/6
under Dora Billington and became technical
and teaching assistant in 1947. Built and set up
Ducketts Wood Pottery, Hertfordshire, 1946/7
making slipware, tin-glaze and, later, mosaics.
Started the Pottery Department at
Goldsmiths' College 1948, stonewares, with
Sheila, at potteries in Greenwich, Castle Hill in
Kent, and for fourteen years at Lacock,
Wiltshire. Part-time teaching until 1968 at
Chaucer and Maidstone College of Art. Council
Member of the Craftsmen Potters Association
for several years organising three film festivals.
Made several films with John Anderson
including 'Isaac Button', 'Creatures in Clay'
(Rosemary Wren), 'Raku, English style', 'David
Leach' etc. and issued five hundred slides on
pottery. Books include three in dictionary form
Practical Pottery (3rd Edition 1992), *Pottery
Form* and *Pottery Decoration*, also *Electric Kiln
Construction* etc. Initiated and ran Craft
Potters Association Archives 1975-87. **Sheila
Fournier** trained at Goldsmiths' College,
London and has potted professionally since
1961 making stonewares, inlaid and other
porcelain and some sawdust fired and raku
ware. Made several hundred drawings for the
books.

Sylvia Des Fours   49
Heather Hill
Givons Grove
Leatherhead
Surrey KT22 8LB

Leatherhead (0372) 372473

Visitors welcome by appointment

David Frith   50
Brookhouse Pottery & Malt House Gallery
Brookhouse Lane
Denbigh
Clwyd
North Wales LL16 4RE

Denbigh (0745) 812805

Showroom open 10.00 am-6.00 pm six days
Telephone for Sundays mostly open in season

Margaret Frith   51
Brookhouse Pottery & Malt House Gallery
Brookhouse Lane
Denbigh
Clwyd
North Wales LL16 4RE

Denbigh (0745) 812805

Showroom open 10.00 am-6.00 pm six days
Telephone for Sundays mostly open in season

Tessa Fuchs   52
24 Cross Road
Kingston-upon-Thames
Surrey KT2 6HG

081-549 6906

Visitors by appointment only

Tony Gant   53
53 Southdean Gardens
Southfields
London SW19 6NT

081-789 4518

Trade enquiries welcomed

Carolyn Genders   54
Heatherwood West
Sandy Lane
Crawley Down
Sussex
RH10 4HR

Copthorne (0342) 712987

Visitors welcome to workshop by prior
arrangement

John Gibson   55
Gibson Keramik
Kildevad 6
Østerlars
3760 Gudhjem
Bornholm
Denmark

Tel: Denmark 56498231

We run courses throughout the year dealing
with saltglaze and decoration techniques. Write
for details or telephone Denmark 56498231

Christopher Green 56
34 Northover Road
Westbury-on-Trym
Bristol
Avon
BS9 3LL
(0272) 500852

Visitors by appointment

Ian Gregory 57
The Studio Workshop
Crumble Cottage
Ansty
Dorchester
Dorset DT2 7PN

Milton Abbas (0258) 880891

Workshop is not open to the public, but items can be purchased from the potter from 2.00-6.00 pm weekdays and 9.00 am-6.00 pm weekends

Frank Hamer 58
Llwyn-On
Croes-yn-y-Pant
Mamhilad
Pontypool
Gwent NP4 8RE

Little Mill (049528) 282

Visitors welcome preferably by appointment

Jane Hamlyn 59
Millfield Pottery
Everton
near Doncaster
S. Yorks DN10 5DD

Retford (0777) 817723

Visitors welcome - telephone first if possible

Alan Heaps 60
Minhafren
Aberbechan
Newtown
Powys SY16 3AW
(0686) 630644

The workshop is open at any reasonable time

Joan Hepworth 61
Westcott Pottery
Robin Cottage
Stones Lane
Westcott
near Dorking
Surrey RH4 3QH
Dorking (0306) 880392

Visitors welcome by appointment but does not employ assistants or trainees

Karin Hessenberg 62
72 Broomgrove Road
Sheffield
S10 2NA
(0742) 661610 (home)

128 Robey Street
Sheffield S4 8JG
(studio)

Joanna Howells 63
2 Albion Square
London
E8 4ES
071-249 0760 (work)
081-341 7306 (answerphone)

Visitors welcome by appointment

Anita Hoy 64
50 Julian Avenue
Acton,
London W3 9JF
081-992 4041

Visitors by appointment only

John Huggins 65
Courtyard Pottery
Groundwell Farm
Cricklade Road
Swindon
Wiltshire
Swindon (0793) 727466

Workshop showroom open Monday - Saturday 9.00 am-5.30 pm. Summer Sundays 1-5.00 pm.

John Jelfs 66
The Pottery
Clapton Road
Bourton-on-the-Water
Gloucestershire GL54 2DN
Cotswold (0451) 20173

Showroom open 9.00 am-6.00 pm Monday to Saturday

Chris Jenkins   67
19 Towngate
Marsden
Huddersfield
Yorkshire HD7 6DD

Huddersfield (0484) 844444

Visitors welcome by appointment

Wendy Johnson   68
92 Nottingham Road
New Basford
Nottingham
NG7 7AH

(0602) 607940

Hazel Johnston   69
The Croft
North Street
Marton
Rugby
Warwickshire CV23 9RJ

Marton (0926) 632467

Visitors welcome by appointment

David Jones   70
18 Willes Terr.
Leamington Spa
Warwicks.
CV31 1DL

(0926) 314643

Visitors are welcome by appointment only

David Lloyd Jones   71
34 School Lane
Fulford
York YO1 4LS

(0904) 633331

Workshop and showroom open daily
9.00 am-6.00 pm but telephone at weekends

Walter Keeler   72
Moorcroft Cottage
Penallt
Monmouth
Gwent NP5 4AH

Monmouth (0600) 713946

Visitors welcome but please telephone first

Ruth King   73
Rose Cottage
Main Street
Shipton-by-Beningbrough
York YO6 1AB

York (0904) 470196

Visitors welcome by appointment

Gabriele Koch   74
147 Archway Road
London N6 5BL

081-340 4927

Visitors welcome by appointment

Anna Lambert   75
Chapel Road
Steeton
W. Yorks
BD20 6NU

(0535) 657003

Visitors welcome but please write or telephone
first

Nigel Lambert   76
Golden Valley Cottage
Morse Lane
Drybrook
Gloucestershire
GL17 9BA

(0594) 542251

No showroom, but visitors welcome; please
telephone first

Peter Lane   77
Ivy House
Jacklyns Lane
Alresford
Hampshire SO24 9JU

(0962) 735041

Visitors welcome by appointment only

Richard Launder   78
35 St Georges Road
Farnham
Surrey
GU9 8NA

Farnham (0252) 725794

Visitors welcome by appointment only

David Leach OBE   79
Lowerdown Pottery
Bovey Tracey
Devon
TQ13 9LE

(0626) 833408

Visitors are welcome at showroom
9.00 am-6.00 pm weekdays, Saturdays
9.00 am-1.00 pm by appointment only

Janet Leach   80
Leach Pottery
St Ives
Cornwall

Penzance (0736) 796398

Showroom open 10.00 am-5.00 pm weekdays.
Summer season and holidays 10.00 am-5.00
pm. Other times by request

John Leach   81
Muchelney Pottery
nr Langport
Somerset TA10 0DW

(0458) 250324

Shop Open (all year round) Monday-Friday
9.00 am-1.00 pm, 2.00-5.00 pm; Saturday
9.00 am-1.00 pm. Workshop viewing: by prior
telephone appointment please. Kiln Firing: may
be viewed on advertised Open Days.

Eileen Lewenstein   82
11 Western Esplanade
Portslade
Brighton
East Sussex BN41 1WE

Brighton (0273) 418705

Visitors welcome by appointment

Martin Lewis   83
110c Lynncroft
Eastwood
Notts. NG16 3ES

(0773) 710501

No showroom; visitors welcome but please
telephone first

Mal Magson   84
45 North Leas Avenue
Scarborough
North Yorkshire YO12 6LJ

Scarborough (0723) 362969

Visitors by appointment only

John Maltby   85
The Orchard House
Stoneshill
Crediton, Devon
EX17 4EF

Crediton (0363) 772753

Visitors welcome at any reasonable time.
Please telephone first

West Marshall   86
118 White Hill
Chesham
Buckinghamshire
HP5 1AR

Chesham (0494) 785969

Very small workshop - visitors by appointment
only please

Will Levi Marshall   87
c/o Alfred University
Ceramic Art Department
Alfred, N.Y. 14802
U.S.A.

607 871 2458

Leo Francis Matthews   88
Ivy Court
Shawbury
Nr Shrewsbury
Shropshire

Shawbury (0903) 250 866

Visitors by appointment only

Peter Meanley   89
6 Downshire Road
Bangor
Co. Down
N. Ireland
BT20 3TW

Bangor (0247) 466831

Visitors welcome, but please telephone first

Eric James Mellon   90
5 Parkfield Avenue
Bognor Regis
West Sussex
PO21 3BW

Pagham (0243) 263221

Clients by appointment

Jon Middlemiss 91
Wheal Vor Cottage
Tyringham Road
Lelant, St Ives
Cornwall TR26 3LF

(0736) 754832

Visitors by appointment only

David Miller 92
Collorgues
30190
Nr Uzes
France

(33) 66.81.91.19

and

33 St Andrew's Square
Surbiton
Surrey, KT6 4EG

Visitors welcome; write or telephone
beforehand

Ursula Mommens 93
The Pottery
South Heighton
Newhaven
Sussex
BN9 0HL

(0273) 514330

Open every day 9 am-6 pm

Emily Myers 94
68 Kensington Park Road
London
W11 3BJ

071-727 5942

Laurence McGowan 95
6 Aughton
Collingbourne Kingston
Marlborough
Wilts.
SN8 3SA

Collingbourne (0264) 850 749

Visits by appointment please

Susan Nemeth 96
Workshop:
27-29 Union Street
London SE1

071-407 0009

Correspondence please to:
53a Stoke Newington Church Street
London N16 0AR

071-249 0102

Magdalene Anyango N Odundo 97
contact: c/o CPA
William Blake House
Marshall Street
London
W1V 1FD

Lawson Oyekan 98
7 Cotswold Gardens
East Ham
London E6 3HZ

081-472 6976

Colin Pearson 99
3 Mountfort Terrace
Barnsbury Square
London N1 1JJ

071-607 1965

Workshop & Gallery
15-17 Cloudesley Road
London N1 0EL

Attendance is irregular so please telephone
first. The workshop is a short walk from the
Angel, Islington and five minutes walk from the
new Crafts Council Gallery. Cars should
approach via Copenhagen Street. Parking is
easy in Cloudesley Road.

Jane Perryman 100
102 Sturton Street
Cambridge CB1 2QF

(0223) 312301

Visitors are welcome by appointment only

Richard Phethean 101
23 Rollscourt Avenue
London SE24 0EA

071-737 3783

Anthony Phillips 102
23a Iliffe Yard
Crampton Street
London SE17 3QA

071-703 1490

Visitors welcome by appointment

Peter Phillips   103
Ivy Cottage
Taylors Lane
Trottiscliffe, Kent
ME19 5DS

Fairseat (0732) 822901

La Reynie
Murcurol
Commune de Borreze
Salignac 24590
Dordogne
France

33.53.28.93.31

Visitors welcome, by appointment, at either studio

Mick Pinner   104
West Meon Pottery
Church Lane
West Meon, Petersfield
Hants.
GU32 1JW

West Meon (0730 829) 434

Visitors are welcome, preferably by appointment

John Pollex   105
White Lane Gallery
1 White Lane
Barbican
Plymouth, Devon
PL1 2LP

Plymouth (0752) 662338

Gallery open throughout the year
10.00 am-5.00 pm. Visitors to the workshop can do so by appointment

Vicki Read   106
'Church Green'
Bickleigh
Tiverton
Devon EX16 8RH

Bickleigh (0884) 855 657

Stanislas Reychan MBE   107
757 The White House
Albany Street
London NW1 3UP

071-387 1200

Modelled figures and ornaments. Born 1897. Trained at St Martin's School of Art and Central School of Arts and Crafts under Dora Billington. Has exhibited at the Royal Academy, Design Centre and has had many one-man shows. Paris Salon Bronze Medal 1958, Silver Medal 1960. Honorary Member CPA and National Society of Painters and Sculptors. Retired 1985.

Mary Rich   108
Penwerris Pottery
Cowlands Creek
Old Kea
nr Truro
Cornwall TR3 6AT

Truro (0872) 76926

There is no showroom, but visitors are welcome by prior appointment

Christine-Ann Richards   109
Chapel House
The Street
Wanstrow
Shepton Mallet
Somerset BA4 4TB

(074 9850) 208

Visitors to workshop by appointment only

David Roberts   110
Cressfield House
44 Upperthong Lane
Holmfirth
Huddersfield
West Yorkshire HD7 1BQ

Huddersfield (0484) 685110

No showroom but visitors are welcome to workshop by appointment

Sara Robertson   111
15 Finsen Road
London
SE5 9AX

071-274 4169

(Studio: 071-708 5904)

Jim Robison   112
Booth House Gallery
3 Booth House
Holmfirth
Huddersfield
W. Yorkshire HD7 1QA

Huddersfield (0484) 685270

Studio and Gallery open to the public at weekends and by appointment

Phil Rogers   113
Marston Pottery
Lower Cefn Faes
Rhayader, Powys
LD6 5LT

Rhayadar (0597) 810875

Workshop and showroom ½ mile from village centre. Signposted from car park. Visitors welcome at the workshop at any reasonable time

Duncan Ross   114
Daneshay House
Alma Lane, Hale
Farnham, Surrey
GU9 0LT

Farnham (0252) 710704

Visitors welcome by appointment

Fiona Salazar   115
79 Redston Road
London N8 7HL

081-341 1672

Visitors welcome by appointment only

Antonia Salmon   116
20 Adelaide Road
Nether Edge
Sheffield
S7 1SQ

0742 585971

Visitors welcome by appointment only

Patrick Sargent   117
Nyffel
4950 Huttwil
Switzerland

(010 41) 63 723390

Visitors welcome by prior arrangement. Students genuinely interested in wood firing are occasionally accepted for short periods

Micki Schloessingk   118
Bridge
Cheriton
Gower
W. Glamorgan SA3 1BY

(0792) 386279

Visitors are very welcome to the workshop but please telephone first

David Scott   119
33 Cross Lane
Mountsorrel
Leics. LE12 7BU

Leicester (0533) 302100

Visitors welcome by appointment

Ray Silverman   120
35 Dunster Crescent
Hornchurch
Essex RM11 3QD

Hornchurch (0708) 458864

Visitors by appointment

Michael Skipwith   121
Lotus Pottery
Stoke Gabriel
Totnes
S. Devon TQ9 6SL

Stoke Gabriel (080428) 303

Workshop and showroom open Monday to Friday 9.00 am-5.30 pm and usually on Saturday mornings 9.00 am-1.00 pm

Alison Small   122
5 Raymend Road
Bristol BS3 4QR

Bristol (0272) 635485

Visits by appointment please

Frank Smith   123
Old Winders House
Peasmarsh
Rye
Sussex TN31 6YJ

Peasmarsh (079 721) 284

House easily found on A268 four miles from Rye. Visitors welcome at any time

Peter Smith 124
Higher Bojewyan
Pendeen
Penzance
Cornwall TR19 7TR

Penzance (0736) 788820

Visitors welcome

John Solly 125
Goldspur Cottage
Flackley Ash
Peasmarsh, Rye
East Sussex TN31 6YH

Peasmarsh (079 721) 276

The Pottery is opposite the Flackley Ash
Hotel, on A268, about 50 yards from Frank
Smiths' Pottery. Visitors are welcome at any
reasonable time, but if coming from afar,
please telephone first

Peter Stoodley 126
Little Rings
Buckland Rings
Sway Road
Lymington
Hants. SO41 8NN

Lymington (0590) 79778

Visitors welcome by appointment

Harry Horlock Stringer 127
Taggs Yard School of Ceramics
11½ Woodlands Road, Barnes
London SW13 0JZ

081-876 5750

Visits arranged by telephone appointments only

Helen Swain 128
8 Fyfield Road
Waltham Forest
London E17 3RG

081-520 4043

This is a one woman pottery, at home, so
visitors by appointment only and, sorry, no
students possible

Sutton Taylor 129
Ravenstones
Mount Pleasant North
Robin Hoods Bay
Nr Whitby
North Yorkshire YO22 4RE

0947 880614

Workshop open to visitors by appointment

Sabina Teuteberg 130
86 Cecilia Road
London E8 2ET

071-241 5279

Visitors welcome, but by appointment only

Owen Thorpe 131
Churchstoke Pottery
Old School
Castle Street
Churchstoke
Powys SY15 6AG

Churchstoke (0588620) 511
Chirbury (093 872) 618

Open 9.30 am-2.00 pm
Other times by appointment

Vera Tollow 132
Delmonden Oasthouse
Horns Hill
Hawkhurst
Kent TN18 4XD

(0580) 752270

Visitors welcome by appointment

Marianne de Trey 133
The Cabin
Shinners Bridge
Dartington, Totnes
Devon TQ9 6JB

(0803) 862046 (after 6pm)

Visitors preferably by appointment

Judy Trim 134
3 Coningham Mews
London W12 9QW

081-749 1190

Occasional visitors by appointment only

Ruthanne Tudball 135
Norfolk House
344 Wokingham Road
Earley, Reading
Berks. RG6 2DE

(0734) 68003

I have no showroom but visitors are welcome
to the workshop by appointment only

Tina Vlassopulos 136
29 Canfield Gardens
London NW6 3JP
071-624 4582
Visitors by appointment

Alan Wallwork 137
Whitty Down Farm
Higher Rocombe
Uplyme
Lyme Regis
Dorset DT7 3RR
Lyme Regis (0297) 443508
Visitors are welcome but not too early. A
prior phone call in the evening is a good idea.
I'm usually here but don't always hear the
telephone in the daytime

Josie Walter 3
Pottery Workshop
via Gellia Mill
Bonsall
Derbyshire DE4 2AJ
0629 825178
Visitors always welcome. Please telephone to
check we are there

Sarah Walton 139
Keepers
Selmeston
nr Polegate
East Sussex BN26 6UH
Ripe (0323) 811517 Work
Ripe (0323) 811284 Home
Visitors are welcome to see a display of work
at my workshop. Please telephone beforehand

John Ward 140
Fachongle Uchaf
Cilgwyn
Newport
Dyfed SA42 0QR
Newport (0239) 820 706
Visitors by appointment

Sasha Wardell 141
Le Peyroux
Chabrignac
19350 Juillac
Correze
France
(010 33) 55 25 61 10
Visitors welcome by appointment

Robin Welch 142
Robin Welch Pottery
Stradbroke
Eye
Suffolk IP21 5JP
Stradbroke (0379384) 416
Open 9.00 am-6.00 pm everyday

John Wheeldon 143
18 Oakerthorpe Road
Bolehill
Matlock
Derbyshire DE4 4GP
(0629) 822356
No showroom, but visitors are very welcome -
please telephone first

David White 144
4 Callis Court Road
Broadstairs
Kent CT10 3AE
Thanet (0843) 863145
No showroom, but please telephone

Mary White 145
Zimmerplatzweg 6
6551 Wonsheim
Germany
06703/2922
Visitors welcome, but please telephone first

Caroline Whyman 146
Unit 25, Sumner Workshops
80 Sumner Road
London SE15 6LA
071-708 5904
Workshop open Monday-Friday
10.00 am-5.00 pm. Please telephone first.
Wheelchair access available during these times.
Weekends by appointment.

David Winkley 147
Vellow Pottery
Lower Vellow
Williton
Taunton
Somerset TA4 4LS
Stogumber (0984) 56458
Workshop and pottery open to visitors from
8.30 am until 6.00 pm Monday to Saturday

Mollie Winterburn 148
Tan Cnwch
Ystrad Meurig
Dyfed SY25 6AB
Pontrhydfendigaid (097 45) 275

Mary Wondrausch 149
The Pottery
Brickfields
Compton, nr Guildford
Surrey GU3 1HZ

(0483) 414097

Mon-Fri, 9.00 am-5.00 pm; Sat and Sun
2.00-5.00 pm

Gary Wood 150
35 King Street
Wigton
Cumbria CA7 9EJ

(06973) 42369

Visitors welcome by appointment

Nigel Wood 151
28 Hyde Street
Winchester
Hants SO23 7DX

Winchester (0962) 855463

Steve Woodhead 152
65 Shakespeare Gardens
Rugby
Warwickshire CV22 6HA

0788 522178

Visitors welcome, but please telephone first

Gary Wornell 153
The Old Slaughterhouse
Park Road
Aldeburgh
Suffolk IP15 5EU

Aldeburgh (0728) 453315

My gallery is an extension of my studio, and
visitors are welcome at any time of year by
appointment

**Rosemary D Wren ARCA and Peter M
Crotty** 154
The Oxshott Pottery
Nutwood Steading
Strathpeffer
Ross & Cromarty IV14 9DT

(0997) 421478

Visitors are welcome but please telephone
first. Strathpeffer - a Victorian spa - is 20 miles
N.W. of Inverness on the A834. Take the
M9/A9 from Stirling and turn off through
Dingwall; the Nutwood drive is on the R. just
before the 30 mph sign. Or fly Heathrow -
Inverness (Danair, £69. return in winter)
London, by road — 571 miles

Muriel P Wright 155
Ashanwell
Potkins Lane
Orford, Woodbridge
Suffolk IP12 2SS

(0394) 450580

Oxidised stoneware, glazed white with blue
decoration. Lamps, bowls, dishes and fountain
bowls. Trained at Manchester College of Art.
Potting for over 30 years. Founder member of
CPA. Visitors welcome but telephone call
essential

Takeshi Yasuda 156
c/o Liverpool Polytechnic
School of Arts, Media & Design
68 Hope Street
Liverpool L1 9EB

051-231 2137 (Mon-Fri 9.00 am-7.00 pm)
Fax 051-709 9643

Joanna and Andrew Young 157
A & J Young Pottery
Common Farm
Sustead Road
Lower Gresham
Norfolk NR11 8RE

Malaske (026 377) 548

Small shop now open at Common Farm every
weekday. For weekend opening times and
directions please telephone

Monica Young 158
Old Butcher's Yard
Reeth
Richmond
North Yorkshire DL11 6SP

Richmond (0784) 84487

Visitors by appointment

261

Addresses of Professional Members

Billy Adams 159
3C The Walk
Roath
Cardiff
South Glamorgan CF2 3AF

(0222) 498099

Visitors welcome but please telephone first

Marilyn Andreetti 160
Belle Vue
16 Gews Corner
Cheshunt
Herts EN8 9BX

(0992) 39969

Visitors always welcome but please telephone first

Elizabeth Aylmer 161
Widgery House
20 Market Street
Hatherleigh
Devon EX20 3JP

(0837) 810624

Shop and Showroom open daily, but please telephone out of season

Sylph Baier 162
Tin Star Studio
38 Cheltenham Place
Brighton
Sussex BN1 4AB

(0273) 682042

Visitors are welcome by appointment

Richard Baxter 163
Old Leigh Studios
61 High Street
Leigh-on-Sea
Essex SS9 2EP

(0702) 470490

Open every day 11.30am-5.30pm

John Berry 164
45 Chancery Lane
Beckenham
Kent BR3 2NR

081-658 0351

Suzanne Bergne 165
66 Barkston Gardens
London SW5 0EL

071-373 0668

Visitors are welcome to see work in London or at the studio. Please make a prior appointment

Gillian Bliss 166
32 Talbot Street
Canton
Cardiff

(0222) 373626

Visitors by appointment please

Keith Booth 167
100 King Edward Road
Maidstone
Kent ME15 6PL

(0622) 683816

Visitors by appointment only

Richard Boswell 168
The Malthouse
Bridgefoot Path
Emsworth
Hampshire PO10 7EB

Fareham (0329) 284701

Visitors welcome. Advisable to telephone previous evening

David Brown 169
Highway Cottage
Church Street
Merriott
Somerset

(0460) 75655

Visitors welcome but please telephone first

Jenny Browne 170
Shaftesbury Studios
47 Tyneham Road
London SW11 5XH

Visitors by appointment please

Tony Carter 171
Low Road
Debenham
Stowmarket
Suffolk IP14 6QU

(0728) 860475

Pottery and shop open to visitors Monday-
Saturday who may see work in production and
purchase both firsts and seconds

Tom Chamberlain 172
Yew Tree House
Southend
Bradfield
Reading RG7 6JL

(0734) 744118

Trevor Chaplin 173
Marridge Hill Cottage
Ramsbury
Marlborough
Wilts. SN8 2HG

Linda Chew 174
42 Cheriton Road
Winchester
Hants SO22 5AY

(0962) 867218

Visitors welcome but please telephone first

Desmond Clover 175
Clover Pottery
5 Oldhurst Road
Pidley
Huntingdon
Cambs PE17 3BY

(0487) 841 026

Shop open every day 8.30am to 7pm, if
travelling any distance, telephone first.

Elaine Coles 176
Elaine Coles Ceramics
Country Gardens Garden Centre
London Road
Windlesham
Surrey GU20 6LL

(0344) 874181

Open Wednesday — Sunday 10am-5pm.
Visitors are welcome.

Jo Connell 177
Witherley Lodge
12 Watling Street
Witherley
Atherstone
Warwickshire CV9 1RD

(0827) 712128

Visitors welcome by appointment. Some work
always on display, commissions accepted.

Molly Curley 178
32 South Rise
Llandishen
Cardiff CF4 5RH

(0222) 756428

Louise Darby 179
Redhill Farmyard
Redhill
Alcester
Warwickshire B49 6NQ

(0789) 765214

Nick Douglas 180
34 Fore Street
Bere Alston
Yelverton
Devon PL20 7AD

Tavistock (0822) 841220

Visitors by appointment

Bridget Drakeford 181
Studio 1
Jinney Ring Centre
Hanbury, Bromsgrove
Worcestershire B60 4BU

(0527) 821676

Visitors welcome by appointment

Victoria and Michael Eden 182
Parkside
Hale
nr. Milnthorpe
Cumbria LA7 7BL

(05395) 62342

Kirsti Buhler Fattorini 183
5 Broadway
Hale
Cheshire WA15 0PF

061-980 4504

Visitors by appointment

263

Judith Fisher   184
Huntswood
St. Helena's Lane
Streat
Sussex BN6 8SD

(0273) 890088

Visitors by appointmnent

Alan Gaff   185
Argyll Pottery
Dalrannoch
Barcaldine
By Oban
Argyll PA37 ISQ

Ledaig (0631 72) 503

Showroom open daily Monday-Friday
10am-6pm

Liz Gale   186
Taplands Farm Cottage
Webbs Green
High Street
Soberton
Hampshire SO3 IPY

(0705) 632686

Visitors welcome but please telephone first

Philip Gardiner Pottery   187
8 Fore Street
Mevagissey
Cornwall PL26 6UQ

(0726) 842042

The pottery/shop is in the centre of
Mevagissey. Open daily from Easter to
Christmas

Rodney George   188
The Garden House
Thames Road
Goring-on-Thames
Reading
Berks. RG8 9AH

(0491) 873276

Graham Glynn   189
Ashlea Cottage
Llanddona
Beaumaris
Anglesey
Gwynedd LL58 8UD

(0248) 810592

Visitors by appointment

Paul Green   190
Abbey Pottery
Cerne Abbas
Dorchester
Dorset DT2 7JQ

Cerne Abbas (0300) 341865

Wholesale and retail customers always
welcome. Showroom open 7 days a week
9.30am-6pm. Closed some Mondays in winter
so please phone

Dimitra Grivellis   191
Unit 9
Metropolitan Workshps
Enfield Road
London NI 5AZ

071-249 5455

Visitors welcome but please telephone first

Frauke Güntzel   192
Pottery in 'Harpers' Garden Centre
The Reeds
Frensham
Surrey GU10 3BP

Workshop open Tuesday-Sunday 10am-6pm.
Visitors welcome

Morgen Hall   193
Studio 5
Chapter Arts Centre
Market Road
Canton
Cardiff CF5 IQE

(0222) 396061 ext. 219
(0222) 238716

Visitors always welcome at workshop, but
please telephone first

Janet Halligan   194
Oak Bank Farm
Wybunbury Road
Willaston
Nantwich
Cheshire CW5 7ER

(0270) 665703

Visitors welcome but please telephone first

264

Michael and Barbara Hawkins 195
The Pottery
Rooksmoor Mills
Bath Road
Stroud
Glos. GL5 5ND

(045 387) 3322

Showroom is open 7 days a week 10-4
All visitors welcome

Chrisopher Helson 196
Contact Address
14 Ash Tree Avenue
Nettleham
Lincoln LN2 2TQ

(0522) 751380
(0423) 879466 Ext 230

Terri Holman 197
The Rainbow Pottery
Rainbow
Avenue Road
Torquay TQ2 5TG

Torquay (0803) 295277

Ashley Howard 198
10 Pine Grove
Maidstone
Kent

(0622) 686390

Visitors welcome by appointment

Eileen Jones 199
45 Dobbins Lane
Wendover
Aylesbury
Bucks HP22 6DH

(0296) 622094

Vresh David Kanikanian 200
Gallery Tavid
56 St. Mary's Road
London W5 5EX

081-566 1494

Visitors welcome, but please telephone first

Jonathan Keep 201
JK Pottery
31 Leiston Road
Knodishall
Saxmundham
Suffolk IP17 1UQ

(0728) 823901

Visitors welcome Monday-Saturday
9am-5.30pm. Advisable to telephone if
travelling long distances

Julian King-Salter 202
Bancau
Brynberian
Crymych
Dyfed SA41 3TS

023 979 652

Visitors welcome to the workshop by
appointment

Kirton Pottery 203
36 High Street
Kirton in Lindsey
Gainsborough
Lincs. DN21 4LX

(0652) 648867

Gaynor Lindsell 204
Whalebones
Wood Street
Barnet
Herts. EN5 4BZ

081-449 5288

Christine McCole 205
Hafod Hill Pottery
Llanboidy
Whitland
Dyfed SA34 0ER

Visitors welcome

Vinitha McWhinnie 206
22 Widney Manor Road
Solihull
West Midlands B91 3JQ

021-705 8842

Visitors by appointment only

Made in Cley 207
High Street
Cley-next-the-Sea
Norfolk NR25 7RF

(0263) 740134

Visitors welcome at the gallery all year round

Fenella Mallalieu 208
100 Mortimer Road
London N1 4LA

071-241 6553

Angela Mellor 209
5 Sculpfield Road
Grantchester
Cambridge CB3 9NL

(0223) 840528

Visitors by appointment

Kate Mellors 210
'Rosemead'
Marshwood
Nr. Bridport
Dorset DT6 5QB

(02977) 217

Visitors welcome but please telephone first

Toff Milway 211
Conderton Pottery
The Old Forge
Conderton
Nr. Tewkesbury
Glos. GL20 7PP

(0386) 89387

Jill Moger 212
The Studio
75 Millfield Lane
Nether Poppleton
York YO2 6NA

(0904) 794874

Studio visits by appointment

Roger Mulley 213
Clanfield Pottery
131 Chalton Lane
Clanfield
Waterlooville
Hampshire PO8 0RG

(0705) 595144

Visitors always welcome at weekends

Sue Munday 214
The Workshop
53 Anderson Avenue
Earley
Reading
Berkshire RG6 1HD

(0734) 265063

Stephen Murfitt 215
The Old Police House
Devizes Road
Upavon
Pewsey
Wilts. SN9 6ED

Stonehenge (0980) 630177

Visitors are welcome by appointment

Tessa Wolfe Murray 216
2 Spenser Road
London SE24 0NR

071-733 9822

Christine Niblett 217
Sa Cantera
Calle Pastoritx
Son Vida
07013 Palma de Mallorca
Spain

(71) 791787

Only 10 minutes from centre of Palma. Visitors welcome but best to telephone first

Jacqueline Norris 218
House of Prayer Pottery
Britwell Road
Burnham
Bucks. SL1 8DQ

(0628) 660984

Visitors welcome but advisable to telephone first

Carol Peever 219
76 Park Lane
Wednesbury
West Midlands WS10 9PT

021-556 0247

Visitors (occasional) by appointment please

Nancy Pickard 220
109 Mackintosh Place
Roath
Cardiff CF2 4RN

(0222) 493658

Visitors welcome by appointment

Philomena Pretsel 221
Rose Cottage
10 Fountain Place
Loanhead
Midlothian EH20 9EA

031-440 0751

Workshop at home, five miles from Edinburgh, with visitors welcome by appointment

Ursula Morley Price 222
Flat 4
34 The Esplanade
Seaford, Sussex

Visitors welcome by appointment

Audrey Richardson 223
Neatham Mill Workshops
Holybourne
Alton
Hampshire GU34 4ET

(0420) 542021
(0306) 882008 (Home)

Visitors welcome by appointment

Michael and Wendy Salt 224
Aislaby Pottery
Aislaby
Pickering
North Yorkshire YO18 8PE

Pickering (0751) 74128

Showroom open daily

Caroline Seaton 225
Amberley Village Pottery
Church Street
Amberley
Nr. Arundel
West Sussex

(0798) 831876

Open most days, all year round from 11am-5.30pm in summer and 11am-4pm in winter

Sheila Seepersaud-Jones 226
5 Brookland Rise
London NW11 6DN

Ifigenija Simonović 227
21 Crownhill Road
Woodford Bridge
Essex IG8 8JF

081-505 7679

Peter Sparrey 228
90 Worcester Road
Link Top
Malvern WR14 1NY

(0684) 568993
(0531) 640064

Chris Speyer 229
Yerja Ceramics & Textiles
Mill Rise
Ford Road
Bampton
Devon EX16 9LW

(0398) 331163

Visitors welcome but telephone first

Christel Spriet 230
The Hermitage
35 College road
Framlingham
Suffolk IP13 9ER

(0728) 724333

Rebecca Taylor 231
18 Clarion House
St. Anne's Court
Soho
London W1V 3AX

071-434 2924

Lyndon Thomas 232
Swn y Môr
Llanarth
Aberaeron
Dyfed SA47 0PZ

(0545) 580406

Visitors welcome by appointment

Katrina Trinick   233
Lesquite
Lanivet·
Bodmin
Cornwall PL30 5HT

Bodmin (0208) 831716

Visitors welcome, but please telephone first

Clare Parsons Trucco   234
107 Marchmont Road
Edinburgh EH9 1HA

031-447 2424

Visitors welcome but please telephone first

Tydd Pottery   235
Pode Hole
Spalding
Lincs. PE11 3QA

Sue Varley   236
54 Elthorne Road
Uxbridge
Middlesex UB8 2PS

(0895) 231738

Visitors welcome but please telephone first

Carol Wainwright   237
28 Firgrove Hill
Farnham
Surrey GU9 8LQ

(0252) 722998

Visitors welcome but please telephone first

Nicola Werner   238
Old Parsonage
Hemyock
Nr. Cullompton
Devon EX15 3RG

(0823) 680957

Visitors welcome but by appointment only

George Wilson   239
48B Mulgrave Road
Ealing
London W5 1LE

081-998 4470

Visitors welcome by appointment

Gill Wright   240
52 South Street
Epsom
Surrey KT18 7PQ

(0372) 723908

Visitors very welcome but please telephone for appointment first

Becoming A Potter

Ceramic Opportunities in the United Kingdom

The opportunities for studying ceramics are many and varied, ranging from full-time courses in art departments in polytechnics and universities, part-time courses at local institutes, weekends with well known potters to teaching yourself from books and videos. In this section the various possibilities are detailed under different headings.

Courses

Many well established potters offer short courses aimed either at the beginner or the more experienced maker. These may be for one day to two weeks or more. Many of these courses are listed in each issue of *Ceramic Review* and most will supply a brochure outlining what is offered. It is often useful to ask to speak to people who have been on the course if you want a user's view.

Videos and Films

Many videos and films of potters at work are available. They are a good guide to the working methods of individual potters, though no real substitute for a good teacher who can answer questions and deal with your particular needs. However, they are excellent as back-up material.
A free list of available videos and films on craft and design (including ceramics) can be obtained from the Crafts Council, 44a Pentonville Road, London N1 9BY.

Part-time courses

Many BA(Hons) courses are now open to part-time students. In addition local education authorities offer a wide range of part-time courses. Some are classed as 'Non-vocational' but many have been set up to give a first class education so that, over a period of time, they provide a thorough training in studio pottery techniques. Many Art Colleges, Technical Colleges and Colleges of Adult and Further Education (including some of the ones listed here) offer such courses, some giving their own certificate of proficiency. As the intake is irregular and the age and standard of students variable it is usual for each student to follow his/her own course of indefinite duration. Particulars of these and evening institutes in the area can be obtained from your local Adult Education Centre or from the Chief Education Officer of your Education Authority.

Local education authorities also provide evening and day part-time courses for beginners and also for more advanced students. Classes last approximately 2 hours. Fees are relatively low and may be free for people out of work. Basic materials are provided and finished work can be purchased at a minimal cost. Personal tools are not usually supplied. Instructors vary in skill and teaching ability and it is worth asking other students how they have fared. Full information on available classes can be obtained from your local Public Library or Education Office. In London the booklet *Floodlight* lists all currently available classes and can be obtained through most newsagents and bookshops. New sessions start in September each year. It is worth remembering that pottery classes are usually the most popular so book early. However, some vacant places will occur during the year which can be taken up by new students.

Workshop Training

Because of the very diverse nature of studio pottery few formal apprenticeship schemes exist for training prospective potters at present, though with the introduction of National Vocational Qualifications (NVQs) by the government some nationally recognised basis will be set up. The kind of work undertaken by trainees, and the amount and quality of the teaching they receive in the studio of the individual potter will depend largely on the skill and outlook of the potter they work for, and the agreement that is made. While few potters will, or are able, to offer a full time, two-year training, many will take an assistant for a few days or weeks for specific projects.

Joining a workshop requires determination and a degree of luck. The number of potters employing assistants is small, demand for places often exceeds supply, and competition is, therefore, fierce. Success in finding a potter to work with whose pots you admire will require commitment, strong perseverance and almost certainly some measure of being in the right place at the right time.

You can try to join a pottery direct as a trainee assistant with little or no previous experience, or for a period of workshop practice following an art school ceramics course. One with a strong bias towards studio pottery would be an advantage.

The work of some potters is so individual that it almost precludes additional help. Those who do employ assistants often spend much of their time making repetition ware, decorative or functional. Students leaving art schools for workshops may find the change constricting and it is best to bear this in mind. Much of the learning will inevitably be done by making pots designed initially by the potters and the opportunities for personal expression are likely to be limited.

There are no standard rates of pay for trainees and remuneration will be set according to their means in relation to the real productive help that an assistant can give. It is the experience of many potters that assistants often overestimate their ability to make pots quickly and of a saleable quality. Some potters regard the training as payment. The Crafts Council offer a variety of Training Grant Schemes. Some are intended for established craftworkers and these are a great help in supplementing the wages of trainees. But this scheme is not automatically available to every potter with assistants and it must be assumed that rate of pay for trainees will be less — and in some cases considerably less — than those in industry or teaching.

The names and addresses of Fellows and Professional members of the Craft Potters Association are listed in this book. Many other potters are included in 'Visiting Craft Workshops' published by Rural Development Commission. A list of potters who work with assistants can be obtained from the Crafts Council. Regional Art Boards usually have a Craft Officer who can give useful advice on opportunities available in the area.

Application to Studios

Before applying to a potter see the work of as many potters as you can so that you are clear about the kind of pots you want to make. If, for example, your main interest is ceramic sculpture you are likely to be happier working with a potter whose prime interest this is than one preoccupied with domestic ware. Just writing a letter which says, in essence, 'I am interested in pottery. Do you have a job?' is unlikely to gain a positive response. Potters get many such letters from applicants who appear to post a dozen or so at a time to widely differing potters in the hope that something will turn up.

The better, and probably only, way is to go and see the potters of your choice in their studios. This requires a lot of effort, it's time-consuming and demands perseverence mentioned earlier. But in seeking a workshop place you are, in effect, asking potters to make a commitment to you in time, energy and money. Potters have livings to earn and they must be as sure as they can that you are really serious about working with them to mutual advantage. In short they have to be convinced that there is something in it for them as well as you.

Before you visit, telephone or write to see that it is convenient. Take with you any examples or photographs of pots you have made. Without some evidence it is very difficult for potters to judge an applicant's ability or potential.

Working successfully and harmoniously as a member of a small team, or in conjunction with an individual potter, is as much a question of good personal relationships as the teaching and acquisition of skills. In the search for workshop places, therefore, it is difficult to overestimate the value of personal contact. This works both ways; it enables potters to judge at first hand an applicant's response to the work they do and, equally important, it gives applicants the opportunity to see what facilities are available and to say what they can offer the workshop. Trainees have much to give in enthusiasm for and commitment to working with clay, and in ready willingness to share all the many and sometimes tedious jobs that every workshop has to undertake to produce finished pots.

Courses in art colleges, polytechnics and universities

Graduate level courses BA(Hons)

These three or four year Courses (full time) preceded by a one or two year Foundation Course aim for the development of the individual rather than his/her training for a specific employment situation. Entry is highly competitive and educational requirements stringent (usually 5 GCE 'O' level passes or GCSES although some colleges demand one or two 'A' level passes). Pottery (Ceramics) is usually contained in three dimensional design and courses may include work in other media and Art History and Complementary Studies. In the Colleges offering Ceramics as a chief study the emphasis varies widely between craft, fine-art and industrial design pottery. Intending students should study prospectuses or visit courses before making application.

For residents in the UK grants for these courses are mandatory, once a place has been secured, but are subject to means test and other certain conditions. Overseas students may have to pay full fees.

Vocational courses and BTEC

These courses differ from the above in these respects:

● Entry requirements are usually less stringent.

● Courses are geared more towards professional training for subsequent employment as a technician, craftworker, designer/craftworker or designer.

● Grants are at the discretion of the LEAs.

● Courses vary from 2 - 4 years.

● Courses, which usually lead to a local, regional or professional Diploma or Licentiateship include some ancillary studies in drawing, design and other craft techniques.

No official 'sandwich' courses for studio potters exist at present but some Colleges make informal arrangements for students to work in potters' workshops during the course or in vacations.

Colleges offering courses in ceramics

College	Course, entry requirements & qualifications and description of course supplied by college

ENGLAND

Amersham	**Amersham & Wycombe College** Stanley Hill Amersham Bucks. HP7 9HN Tel: (0494) 721121 Fax: (0494) 431577	Ceramics included as an element in our Art Foundation course, **BTEC General Art & Design courses.** 'A' Level Ceramics — entry GCSE in Art or Ceramics together with portfolio of art and design Evening classes in Pottery. These courses act as feeders to courses of higher education namely HND or B.A. in Ceramics or associate subjects.
Bath	**Bath College of Higher Education** Faculty of Art and Music Sion Hill Place Lansdown Bath BA1 5SF Tel: Bath (0225) 425254 Fax: (0225) 445228	**BA (Hons) Ceramics** The course is designed to equip students with an understanding of contemporary ceramics and an education in the broad range of approaches, techniques, craft skills and industrial processes. Supporting studies offer options to work in other mediums and Complementary Studies develop analytical and critical skills, placing Art and Design activities amongst the other cultural, historical and social practices.
Birmingham	**Birmingham Polytechnic Art & Design Centre** New Corporation Street Birmingham B4 7DX Tel: Birmingham 021 331 5819	**BA(Hons) 3D design CNAA ceramics with glass** 1 year foundation or equivalent 5 'O's. 18+ Minimum

Bradford

Bradford & Ilkley Community College
School of Art, Design, & Textiles
Great Horton Road
Bradford
West Yorkshire BD7 1AY
Tel: (0274) 753239

BTEC National Diploma in Design Crafts (with a Ceramics Strand) The ceramics strand is broadly based. Students are offered contrasting and progressively demanding projects before they are encouraged to define and develop their own interests and concerns.
The course is one of a wide range of National level courses which can lead on to degree level study - including the Bradford Multi Media BA(Hons) Degree.
BA(Hons) Art & Design. A course which allows students to interrelate media areas on a Major Pathway in either Art or Design. Major Pathway: Art students may continue Ceramics with Painting. Major Pathway: Design students may combine Ceramics with Textiles, Surface Pattern.

Brighton

Brighton Polytechnic, Faculty of Art, Design and Humanities
Grand Parade
Brighton BN2 2JY
Tel: Brighton (0273) 679179

BA(Hons) CNAA - wood, metal, ceramics and plastics course. 3 years full time. Normally 1 year foundation + 5 'O's.
Direct entry 2 'A's + 3 'O's.
The course is concerned with the needs and disciplines of the individual artist-craftsperson. Objects stemming from the course may be either expressive, decorative or functional according to each student's experience and response. Idea development and problem solving project work are triggered through the materials using recognised and discovered techniques and a range of visual, historical and other research.

Bristol

Bristol Polytechnic
Faculty of Art, Media & Design
Clanage Road, Bower Ashton
Bristol BS3 2JU
Tel: Bristol (0272) 660222 × 4759

BA(Hons) Ceramics The course provides a broad experience of ceramics; established techniques are studied forming the basis for independent development. Ceramics is part of the faculty wide modular scheme which enables students to take part in an extensive range of practical and theoretical art and design studies. The modules are designed to stimulate interest not only in the intrinsic and expressive qualities of ceramics but also in the exciting areas where complementary disciplines overlap. The final year centres on individual, self directed, programmes of work.

Carlisle

Cumbria College of Art & Design
Brampton Road, Carlisle
Cumbria CA3 9AY
Tel: Carlisle (0228) 25333
Fax: (0228) 514491

BTEC and Design (Crafts) Successful applicants initially select Textiles or Ceramics as their Craft Study Option. Textiles includes: Fabric Printing, Tapestry, Rug-Weaving and Embroidery. Ceramics includes: Throwing, Press Moulding, Hand Building, Slip Casting, Glaze and Kiln Technology. In addition all students will undertake a range of supporting options which may be used in conjunction with their main craft area in the manufacture of a wide range of products. Visual Studies and Contextual Studies support all areas and considerable emphasis is given to Business Studies.

Crewe

Crewe & Alsager College of Higher Education
Crewe Green Road
Crewe
Cheshire CW1 1DU
Tel: (0270) 500661
Fax: (0270) 583433

BA(Hons) Crafts
Combined Studies:
Wood/Metal/Ceramics/Textiles
Course description. The course gives a groundwork in each material in the first half-year, then students choose TWO. It encourages unusual and inventive approaches to working materials and provides opportunities to combine them. Visual and Historical research are integral elements. Also included is a Dissertation, and a Business unit covering basic skills, with a project to plan a hypothetical small business.

Derby

Derbyshire College of Higher Education
Kedleston Road
Derby DE3 1GB
Tel: (0332) 47181
Fax: (0332) 294861

BTEC Higher National Diploma in Design (Crafts) Studio Ceramics Entry requirements: BTEC Diploma in General Vocational Design or General Art and Design or the satisfactory completion of a Foundation Course or a course of an equivalent level or mature students with appropriate experience or students transferring at the end of first year of B.A. course in Ceramics or appropriate industrial experience or, exceptionally, sixth form 'A' level candidates.

Eastbourne

College of Arts & Technology
St Anne's Road
Eastbourne
Sussex BN21 2HS
Tel: Eastbourne (0323) 644711

16+ BTEC General Art and Design
4 GCSE (A, B or C)
2 year General Course, Ceramics specialist design option.
1 year Foundation Course 18+ (3 subjects GCSE at Grade A, B or C Plus 1 A level)

Exeter

**Plymouth Polytechnic
Exeter Faculty of Art and Design**
Earl Richards Road North
Exeter EX2 6AS
Tel: Exeter (0392) 412211

**BA(Hons) Design (3 Dimensional Design)
BA(Hons) Fine Art**

Falmouth

Falmouth School of Art and Design
Woodlane
Falmouth
Cornwall TR11 4RA
Tel: Falmouth (0326) 211077
     Falmouth (0326) 211205

BTEC HND (Design) Ceramics Course content: Visual Studies, Production Studies, Technical Studies, Professional Studies and Contextual Studies.
Introduced through: Throwing, Handforming, Casting and Surface Decoration, which gradually leads to negotiated programmes of study within a specific area of personal interest.
Leading to: Self employment, Employment in Industry, Adult/Special Needs Teaching, Continuing Education

Farnham

West Surrey College of Art and Design
The Hart, Farnham
Surrey
Tel: (0252) 722441

BA(Hons) Ceramics with supporting studies 5 GCSEs Grade C or above. Applicants normally will have successfully completed the Foundation Course or BTEC National Diploma. The School of Ceramics is part of the Department of Design, which embraces Glass, Metal, Woven and Printed Textiles. The School offers a stimulating and challenging environment in which to study Ceramics, with spacious and exceptionally well-equipped studios.

Gloucester

Royal Forest of Dean College
Five Acres Campus
Berry Hil
Coleford
Gloucester GL16 7JT
Tel: (0594) 833416

BTEC National Diploma in Design Ceramics The course is intended to develop the creative, critical and technical ability of individual students to their full potential. Working in both two and three dimensions, the course is designed to equip students with an understanding of a wide range of techniques, materials, craft skills and industrial processes whilst broadening their cultural and historical appreciation of art and design.

Harrogate

Harrogate College of Arts & Technology
Hornbeam Park
Hookstone Road
Harrogate
North Yorkshire HG2 8QT
Tel: (0423) 879466

BTEC National Diploma in Ceramics Full-time or part-time attendance. Entry qualifications: 4 GCSE Passes (or equivalent) Accreditation for prior learning will be considered for mature students. Course includes introductions to handbuilding, throwing, modelling, mouldmaking and Industrial techniques, clay and glaze technology, kiln building (Raku, wood and salt firings) leading to individual specialist involvement in aspects of these practical studies. A Visual Studies programme which includes drawing and colour studies, design studies, surface design and photography; Historical and Contextual Studies together with aspects of Business Studies.

Hereford

Herefordshire College of Art and Design
Art & Design Admissions Registry, (ADAR)
Penn House
9 Broad Street
Hereford HR4 9AP
Tel: (0432) 273359
Fax: (0432) 341099

BTEC Course Description A Course that prepares students for entrance into the professional world of the designer/maker. To achieve this objective the prerequisite skills and knowledge required for the successful running of a small business are directly reflected in the Course philosophy, content and structure both at a practical and theoretical level. Options in: ceramics, metal, textiles. These are supported by a comprehensive range of media, both traditional and non-traditional.

High Wycombe	**Buckinghamshire College of Higher Education, a college of Brunel University** Queen Alexandra Road High Wycombe HP11 2JZ Tel: (0494) 522141	**BA(Hons) Ceramics with Glass** Applicants must have completed Art Foundation Course and be over 18 with 5 GCSEs or 3 GCSEs and one A Level. This exciting course provides a broad-based experience of working with both clay and glass, and students are taught both studio and industrial crafts skills. The aim of the course is to help students develop a personal and visual awareness through working with these materials, thus providing a sound basis for their future development as artists and designers.
Leicester	**Leicester Polytechnic School of Design and Manufacture** PO Box 143 Leicester LE1 9BH Tel: Leicester (0533) 551551	**BA(Hons) Ceramics/Glass** Entry requirements: 5 'O' plus Foundation or BTEC. Do not accept direct entry. Applications from mature students welcome. Each student has the opportunity to work with a variety of media and experience a wide range of attitudes to problem solving. From the very beginning the course is involved with both the practice and theory of design for production as well as the realisation of personal dreams and fantasies. Live projects, national competitions.
London	**Camberwell College of Arts** (The London Institute) Peckham Road London SE5 8UF Tel: 071-703 0987	**BA(Hons) Full-time Course** The course enables students to exploit the medium and to understand and enjoy the versatility of ceramics and the scope it offers for creative thinking, designing and making. The ceramics specialist study is a three year full-time course leading to the award of a BA Honours Degree. It provides for the designing and making of objects in fired clay, in a craft based studio/workshop context.
	Central Saint Martins College of Art and Design (The London Institute) Southampton Row London WC1B 4AP Tel: 071 753 9090 Fax: 071 242 0240	**BA(Hons) Ceramic Design** The course explores functional ceramic design through a wide range of approaches open to the ceramic designer. It produces graduates with a high level of intellectual maturity that makes them eligible for a number of distinctive careers open to the professional ceramist. The course recognises function as having three interrelated aspects: **an audience** for whom the work is intended to be used and enjoyed; **a material base** the materials, production processes and finishes by which the work is made; **a context** both cultural and historical to which every designed object refers providing the framework through which ideas are expressed.

Barnet College
Wood Street
Barnet
Herts EN5 4AZ
Tel: 081-440 6321
Fax: 081-441 5236

**BTEC National Diploma in General
Art & Design.** Full time 2 year diagnostic
Art & Design 16+
**BTEC National Diploma in Design 3D
Studies.** Full time, wood, metal, ceramics,
engineering in application to product design.

Hounslow Borough College
London Road
Isleworth
Middlesex TW7 4HS
Tel: 081-568 0244
Fax: 081-569 7787

Foundation Course, 1 year.
5 'O' levels or GCSE equivalents plus a
good portfolio.
**BTEC Diploma General Art &
Design,** 2 years. 4 'O' levels or GCSE
equivalents plus a good portfolio.

Middlesex University
Cat Hill
Barnet
Herts. EN4 8HT
Tel: 081-368 1299

BA(Hons) Ceramics The Ceramics
modular course offers a full time 3 or 4
year specialist study. A student who wishes
to do a sandwich placement or foreign
exchange in the third year of the course
would complete the course in 4 years.
Students not wishing to do this would
complete in 3 years. Students will be asked
at interview the length of course required
The first year modules in Ceramics involve
the student in learning the essential basic
skills and methods in Handbuilding,
Throwing and Industrial Production, plus an
introduction to Glass.

**University of Westminster
Harrow College**
Northwick Park
Harrow HA1 3TP
Tel: 071 911 5000

3 years Workshop Ceramics BA(Hons)
standard entry with Foundation or BTEC
Diploma. Non-standard entry for mature
students (21+). The Workshop Ceramics
BA(Hons) Course accepts no narrow
definitions of Studio pottery but seeks to
promote excellence and, by the
examination of historical and contemporary
practice and through mastery of related
craft skills, to extend the conceptual
possibilities of the discipline. The particular
philosophy that has evolved at Harrow,
rooted in the acquisition of a sound
understanding of the craft skills and
disciplines as an essential foundation for
personal research and development, has
been well documented and vindicated by
the professional successes of its past
students.

**Loughborough College of Art &
Design**
Radmoor
Loughborough
Leicester LE11 3BT
Tel: (0509) 261515

BA(Hons) Entrance qualifications as
standard but main criteria for acceptance is
portfolio and commitment. As in all Art
and Design degrees 20% of the course is
taken up with academic work and
prospective students should be able to
demonstrate an ability to cope with the
written work. The course is a 3 year
specialist degree in ceramics, there are
support studies in photography and
computers in the structured 1st year, and
this leads progressively into self directed
working in the 2nd and 3rd year.

Lowestoft

School of Art and Design Lowestoft College
St. Peters Street
Lowestoft
Suffolk NR32 2NB
Tel: Lowestoft (0502) 583521

BTEC National Diploma in Ceramic Design
2 years full-time attendance. Requirements: Normally 4 GCSEs at Grade C or above, or equivalent. However, if you are a mature student, or if you can demonstrate some prior knowledge of the subject or have a good portfolio of general art-work which you can present at interview, then we may be able to accept you onto the course with fewer formal qualifications. Practical experience including drawing and visual research; surface pattern design; studio crafts — handbuilding and throwing; industrial ceramics; sculptural ceramics; clay, glaze and kiln technologies; mould-making and kiln building; business and professional studies.

Manchester

Manchester Polytechnic
Faculty of Art and Design
School of Wood, Metal, Ceramics & Glass
Chatham Building
Cavendish Street
Manchester M15 6BR
Tel: 061-247 2000
061-247 1003 (direct line)
Fax: 062-236 0820

BA(Hons) 3D Design, Wood/Metal/Ceramics and Glass. This is a multi-disciplinary course where students can choose Ceramics as their final year main study area. Other students will be specialising in one of the other areas. All students work across a wide area of materials. The course in Ceramics covers Studio, Industrial, Architectural and Fine Art Ceramics leading in the final year to a more individually orientated expression. The course is project based with relevant History and Technology Lectures. Career possibilities — further study at MA level, the teaching profession (including CDT), Designing for Industry, setting up small businesses and workshops, working as artist/ potters.

Middlesbrough

Cleveland College of Art & Design
Green Lane
Middlesbrough
Cleveland TS5 7RJ
Tel: Middlesbrough (0642) 821441

College Certificate in Design Crafts
(ceramics) 3 years part-time. No formal academic qualifications required. Options in wood/furniture and jewellery. Studio Pottery techniques. The course offers personal development in both techniques and aesthetics of contemporary studio ceramics. In common with many other colleges we also run the BETC GAD Foundation Course. This provides a route into full-time higher education courses for students in Cleveland.

Nuneaton

North Warwickshire College
Hinckley Road
Nuneaton CV11 6BH
Tel: (0203) 349321
Fax: (0203) 329056

BETC National Diploma in Design Ceramics Entry by 4 GCSE's and/or portfolio of work demonstrating a commitment to ceramics. A full-time 2 year course designed for students interested in a professional career as a designer/maker/ technician in Ceramics. The aim is to provide students with the skills and knowledge necessary for continued futher education or employment, enabling them to follow a career related to their interests and skills in the design studio of a factory, the ceramic workshop or studio pottery.

Preston

Lancashire Polytechnic Faculty of Design & Technology
Preston PR1 2TQ
Tel: Preston (0772) 201201
Fax: (0772) 892981

BA(Hons) Three Dimensional Design Course Entry requirements: Applicants must be 18 years of age on 31 December in the year of entry and hold: B/TEC Diploma in three-dimensional Design, Design, Crafts, General Vocational Design, or General Art & Design. or A B/TEC Certificate in the above subjects; with additional experience, or Attainments comparable with a B/TEC Diploma, with relevant knowledge and skills, i.e. a Foundation Course in Art & Design or relevant employment experience. Applicants will be required to attend an interview and to present a portfolio of their work. Students opt for either Wood, Metal, Ceramics or Glass at the point of entry to the course, but the flexibility exists.

Rochester

Kent Institute of Art & Design
Rochester-upon-Medway College
Fort Pitt
Rochester
Kent ME1 1DZ
Tel: Medway (0634) 830022

BA(Hons) Three Dimensional Design (Pathways in Ceramics, Interior Architecture and Design Representation) The ceramics pathway will offer a broad and divergent experience of ceramics, investigating established processes and techniques of craft based and industrial ceramics. Design projects which direct the students' experience towards ceramics within architecture and the built environment, public arts, architectural restoration and product design will form a major part of the 2nd year studies, leading to individual, self-directed programmes of study in Year 3.
National Diploma in Design Option in Ceramics, 2 years. Entry requirements: Minimum age 16 years, minimum 3 GCSE/GCE 'O' levels or equivalent plus evidence of art/craft/design study. The course includes a wide range of visual studies including drawing, painting and designing and complementary studies which encourages interest in the historical, social, economical and philosophical aspects of the craft. All techniques are covered.

Rotherham

Rotherham College of Arts and Technology
Eastwood Lane
Rotherham
South Yorks S65 1EG
Tel: Rotherham (0709) 362111

GCSE and City and Guilds courses with options through the General Art and Design, Foundation and Access programmes, for people wishing to specialise in Ceramics through a higher education course.

Stafford

Stafford College
Earl Street
Stafford
Staffordshire ST16 2QR
Tel: Stafford (0785) 223800

City and Guilds Creative Studies, Ceramics. Ceramic Design and Production

Stoke-on-Trent

Staffordshire University
School of Design and Ceramics
Divsion of Ceramic Design
College Road
Stoke-on-Trent ST4 2DE
Tel: 0782 744531
Fax: 0782 745627

HND Design (Ceramics) The course is of two years duration and offers a combination of creative, theoretical and practical learning. It is project based, supported by an extensive programme of practical skills, that include: three dimensional modelling and plaster work, print processes and ceramic manufacture. The course shares, with our other ceramic courses, the finest ceramic facilities available in the UK. It has a very close relationship with the ceramic industry, which enables it to give students the benefit of a work placement which is usually in a design studio.
BA(Hon) Design (Ceramics) This course offers a broadly based programme of study, where students initially acquire a wide range of specialist ceramic skills, before focusing on their chosen area of interest. The course shares, with our other ceramic courses the finest ceramic resources in the UK and probably in Europe, this enables a diverse range of work to be produced which covers all aspects of ceramic practice.

Sunderland

University of Sunderland
School of Arts and Cultural Studies
Backhouse Building
Ryhope Road
Sunderland SR2 7EF
Tel: (091) 5152126

BA(Hons) 3D Design (Glass with Ceramics)

WALES

Cardiff

Cardiff Institute of Higher Education
School of Design
Howard Gardens
Cardiff CF2 1SP
Tel: Cardiff (0222) 551111

BA(Hons) Ceramics

Carmarthen

Carmarthenshire College of Technology & Art
Faculty of Art & Design
Job's Well Road
Carmarthen
Dyfed
Tel: Carmarthen (0267) 233995

BTEC National Diploma in Design (Multi-disciplinary course with a specialist option in ceramics) 2 years: Entry 4 GCSE's. HND Diploma in Design Crafts (with a specialist option in ceramics) 2 years: Entry BTEC Diploma or Certification or Foundation Course.

Newport

Gwent College of Higher Education
Faculty of Art and Design
College Crescent
Caerleon
Newport
Gwent NP6 1XJ
Tel: (0633) 430088
Fax: (0633) 432006

BA(Hons) Fine Art (CNAA validated)
BA(Hons) Graphic Design (CNAA validated) Ceramics can be studied though a system of mandatory and optional access workshops. Advanced ceramic workshop studies can be taken in year two and three in both courses. BA(Hons) Design Studies University of Wales. Ceramics is studied in year one and two and is an option in year three. Normal entry requirement for all BA courses. NB It is thought likely that the courses currently offered in this college will change in 1993/4.

Wrexham

NE Wales Inst Higher Education
Clwyd College of Art & Design
Technology
49 Regent Street
Wrexham
Clwyd LL11 1PF
Tel: 0978 291 955

BTEC HND Design Crafts (Two Years) Course Structure: HND Design Ceramics — Modular Course. Includes: Historical Design and Technique Study, Surface Decoration, Kiln Building Applique/Lamination, Visual Studies.
HND Design Ceramics A broad based course, which enables students to develop a wide range of skills and interests in the fields of Functional, Architectural, Personal and Environmental Ceramics. The use of other materials is encouraged where appropriate. Creative work is backed up by a programme of technical studies, designed to develop a sound knowledge of materials and processes.

SCOTLAND

Aberdeen

Grays School of Art
The Robert Gordons University
Garthdec Road
Aberdeen AB9 2QD
Tel: Aberdeen (0224) 313247

BA(Hons) and BA(CNAA) degrees in Design and Craft; Ceramics/Jewellery as main or subsidiary subject. Entry qualifications: 3 SCE 'H's incl. English + 2 'O's or 2 GCE 'A's incl. English + 3 'O's. Course provides opportunity of carrying out creative formal ideas which investigate two- and three-dimensional composition. Techniques; thrown pottery; slab ware; hand building; slip-casting and press-moulding; designing and making architectural relief tiles and mural panels; methods of surface decoration, colour and glazing and kiln firing

Dundee

Duncan of Jordanston College of Art
School of Design
Perth Road
Dundee DD1 4HT
Tel. Dundee (0382) 23261
FAx: (0382) 27304

Degree course Contemporary Ceramics 3 years normally 2 'A's + 3 'O's or 3 SCE 'H's + 2 SCE 'O's. BA/BA(Hons) Degree. By interview. Direct entry. Foundation or General Art Diploma Normally 3 'A's or 3 SCE 'H's. B-Des. BDes(Hons) Degree

Edinburgh

Edinburgh College of Art
Heriot Watt University
School of Design and Crafts
Applied Arts Department
Lauriston Place
Edinburgh EH3 9DF
Tel: 031 229 9311
Fax: 031 229 0089

Degree Course/Ceramics BA(Hons) 3 SCE 'H's inc. Eng. 2 SCE 'O's (C band or above). 2 GCE 'A's 3 GCE 'O's (inc. Eng. at 'A' or 'O'). The Section aims to provide an input of manipulative skills and technical information running parallel to the development of each student's creative personality. Initially, set projects familiarise the students with a range of hand and machine processes applied to both form and surface design, great emphasis being placed on self programming as the course develops. Clay, glaze and kiln theory and practice are thoroughly covered, and a programme of relevant historical studies is undertaken through lectures, museum visits and personal research.

Glasgow

Glasgow School of Art
167 Renfrew Street
Glasgow G3 6RQ
Tel: Glasgow (041) 332 9797

BA(Hons) BA Design. Academic Requirements Scottish Certificate of Education — 3 Higher Grades (including English and Art) and any other 2 subjects at 'O' Grade. OR General Certificate of Education — 2 'A' levels (including Art and English) and 3 'O' levels. If 'A' level English not obtained, passes at 'O' level required in BOTH English literature and English language. OR Equivalent qualifications including HNC, HND SCOTVEC, DATEC, BTEC and Higher English. Course principally involved in clay and plaster work, but students actively encouraged to experiment with a variety of materials and techniques.

NORTHERN IRELAND

Belfast

University of Ulster
Department of Applied and Decorative Art
York Street
Belfast
Tel: Belfast (0232) 328515

BA(Hons) Fine Craft Design. Study Areas: Ceramics, Silversmiths & Jewellery, Embroidery. This provides a unit based course across the whole Faculty including Design, Fine Art and Textiles/Fashion common to all first year students. This ability to 'specialise' exists in years two and three. Equally, students may wish to extend in second and third year units taken in first year. All courses within the Faculty allow for specialisation or for student breadth. This can permit students to undertake units in other courses.

Post Graduate Courses in Ceramics

Aberdeen

Grays School of Art
The Robert Gordons University
Garthdee Road
Aberdeen AB9 2QD
Tel: Aberdeen (0224) 313247

Post Graduate Diploma Ceramics. 1 year Post Graduate Diploma; BA (CNAA) or equivalent.

Belfast

University of Ulster
Department of Applied and Decorative Art
York Street
Belfast
Tel: Belfast (0232) 328515

P.G. in Applied Arts. Full time 1 year or part time 2 years.

Cardiff

Cardiff Institute of Higher Education
Howard Gardens
Cardiff CF2 1SP
Tel: Cardiff (0222) 551111

PG Dip/MA Ceramics

Edinburgh

Edinburgh College of Art
Heriot Watt University
School of Design and Crafts
Applied Arts Department
Lauriston Place, Edinburgh EH3 9DF
Tel: 031 229 9311
Fax: 031 229 0089

Postgraduate Diploma in Design. The period of study for the Postgraduate Diploma is one academic year (3 terms) and provides opportunity for well-qualified candidates to build on their undergraduate experience through further experimentation, exploration and expression.

Master of Design (MDes) The period of study for the Master's Degree is based on four academic terms (15 months) for the full-time mode with adjustments for part-time, or for a combination of full-time and part-time, study.

Applicants for this research opportunity are required to submit an outline study proposal which identifies the main areas and objectives for study. Following selection, that initial proposal will be developed in consultation with internal and external supervisors.

Glasgow	**Glasgow School of Art** 167 Renfrew Street Glasgow G3 6RQ Tel: Glasgow (041) 332 9797	**One Year Post Graduate Diploma in Ceramics awarded by the School**
London	**Middlesex University** Cat Hill Barnet Herts. EN4 8HT Tel: 081-368 1299	**Post Graduate Certificate** 1 year part time, 2 years full time
	University of London Goldsmiths' College New Cross London SE14 6NW Tel: 081-692 7171 ext. 2121	**College Diploma in Ceramics.** A one year full-time course for students or suitably qualified persons wishing to advance their use of ceramics to a high level.
	Royal College of Art Kensington Gore London SW7 2EU Tel: 071-584 5020	**Royal College of Art MA/MDes./M.Phil** Ceramics & Glass 2 year courses in Designing and making Ceramics and Glass, Architectural Decoration, Design for Ceramics and Glass Industry. Research Projects in Ceramics and Glass, Materials and Technology. Entry Requirements: a first degree or the equivalent experience. Competitive entrance examination February/March each year.
Stoke-on-Trent	**Staffordshire University** School of Design and Ceramics Division of Ceramic Design College Road Stoke-on-Trent ST4 2DE Tel: 0782 744531 Fax: 0782 745637	**Postgraduate Diploma/MA Design (Ceramics)** This linked programme of courses is primarily concerned with ceramic design for small and mass manufacture. The programme offers a one year (34 weeks) postgraduate diploma with the opportunity for progression to either MA full-time or MA sandwich. The full-time route requires in total 53 weeks of continuous study. The sandwich route requires in total two years of full-time study which includes an industrial placement at the beginning of the second year.

Craft Potters Association 1989-92

Exhibitions

1989
Mike Dodd: New Stoneware (February)
Dart Pottery: New Work (March)
Come into the Garden: Pots for Plants, Shrubs, Trees & Flowers, Bird Baths, Sculptures (April)
Takeshi Yasuda: Stoneware (May)
Small is Beautiful: Open Exhibition plus Derek Emms, Derek Clarkson, David Leach, Eileen Lewenstein, Mary Rich (June)
Raku Today: Ian Byers, David Cohen, Christine Constant, Jill Crowley, John Dunn, Dennis Farrell, Keiko Hasekawa, David Howard Jones, David Miller, Anna Noel, Sarah Noel, Tim Proud, David Roberts (July)
High Flyers — Birds in and on Ceramics: Neil Ions, Anna Lambert, John Maltby, Rosemary Wren, Kate Byrne, Jennie Hale, Jeremy James, Laurel Keeley (August)
Feast — Pots for Food: Clive Bowen, Sandy Brown, Peter Dick, Jane Hamlyn, Phil Rogers, Josie Walter, Mary Wondrausch, Andrew and Joanna Young (September)
Janet Leach: New Work (November)
Teapots (November)

1990
Clayworks: CPA Associate Members Exhibition (February)
John Maltby: Recent Work (April)
The New Members Show: Seth Cardew, Margaret Frith, Karin Hessenberg, Emily Myers, Duncan Ross, Antonia Salmon (May)
Anna Lambert: New Pots (June)
Light Fantastic — Porcelain Today: Colin Pearson, Martin Lewis, Russell Coates, Derek Clarkson, Deirdre Burnett, Terry Bell-Hughes, Peter Beard, Ruth Barrett-Danes, Peter Lane, Caroline Wyman, Jane Perryman, Helen Swain and other leading potters (July)
Setting Out: Selected work by Art School Graduates (August)
Ray Finch and Winchcombe Pottery: Wood-fired stoneware and saltglaze (September)
David Leach — Sixty Years a Potter: New stoneware and porcelain (October)
Michael Casson: New Work (November)
Pots for Christmas (December)

1991
Handle with Care: Pots by Members of Northern Potters Association (February)
Tina Vlassopulos: New Work (March)
Geoffrey Fuller: New Work (April)
New Members Show: Tim Andrews, Loretta Braganza, Carlo Briscoe, John Calver, Roger Cockram, Edward Dunn, Christopher Green, Nigel Lambert, Richard Phethean, Mick Pinner, Patrick Sargent, Ruthanne Tudball, Gary Wood (May)

284

Daphne Carnegy: Maiolica (June)
Antonia Salmon: Burnished Earthenware (July)
Setting Out '91: Art School Graduates — 1991 (August)
Phil Rogers: Woodfired Stoneware and Porcelain (October)
Sandy Brown: Ritual Objects — Tableware (October)
John Pollex: New Earthenware (November)

1992
Fireworks: Ceramics by recently elected Professional Members of the Craft Potters Association (February)
Svend Bayer: Wood-fired Pots (March)
Sabina Teuteberg: New Work (April)
Homage to Catalonia: Ceramics from Potters in Catalonia (May)
Patrick Sargent — Touch of Fire (June)
Poetics of Fire: Ceramists associated with Goldsmiths' College (July)
Setting Out: Selected Art School Graduates 1992 (August)
David Roberts: Raku (September)
Crystalline Glazes: Derek Clarkson and other Potters (October)
Peter Beard: New Ceramics (November)

Events and Meetings 1989-1992

1989
Grants and Services — Barclays Price, Crafts Council (May)

1990
Presenting the Professional Potter: Talk and Slides — John Leach, Crafts Council (March)
Setting up a Workshop (Regional Meeting) with David Eeles (May)
American Ceramics — Woody Hughes, Crafts Council (June)
CPA Top Classes: Pottery Workshops, Derby — Josie Walter (July)
Photographing Ceramics — John Anderson, Crafts Council (October)
Meet the New Full Members Chair Emmanuel Cooper, Crafts Council (December)

1991
Chinese Ceramics — Sheila Vainker, British Museum (February and March)
Nature of Influence — Michael Casson, Linnean Society, London (April)
Principles of Prejudice: How and why pots are selected, Chair Emmanuel Cooper, Linnean Society, London (May)
Clayworks II Associates Exhibition Crypt Gallery, St. Martin-in-the-Fields, London (August)
Exhibiting Ceramics — Chris Speyer, Marta Donaghey, Linda Theophulus, Linnean Society, London (October)
60 Years a Potter — David Leach, Linnean Society, London (November)

1992
Percival David Collection of Chinese Ceramics — Talk and guided tour (January)
Images of Africa — Josie Walter, Museum of Mankind, London (February)
Grants and Services — Frances Lord (Regional Meeting) February
Nigerian Pottery — John Leach, East Devon College, Tiverton (May)
Crafts Council Collection: Talk and Slides — Janice Tchalenko, Crafts Council (June)
Photographing Ceramics: Talk, Slides and Workshop — Stephen Brayne, CPA Event at Festival of European Ceramics (July)
Festival of European Ceramics Clayesmore School, Iwerne Minster, Blandford Forum, Dorset (July)
Raku: Talk — David Roberts (October)
Crystalline Glazes: Talk — Derek Clarkson (October)
Egyptian Travels: Talk — Peter Beard (November)

Craft Potters Association of Great Britain Ltd.

Council 1992

Chair	Phil Rogers
Vice-Chair	Josie Walter
Hon. Secretary	Liz Gale
Deputy Hon. Secretary	Tony Gant
	Peter Beard, Emmanuel Cooper, Jack Doherty, Eileen Lewenstein, Jane Perryman, Ruthanne Tudball
Associate Representative	Elizabeth Smith
CPA News Representative	Chris Speyer

Association
Managing Director   Harry Davey

Contemporary Ceramics Craft Potters Shop and Gallery

Manager	Marta Donaghey
Assistant	Ruth Ballard

Ceramic Review

Editors	Eileen Lewenstein, Emmanuel Cooper
Editorial Assistant, Advertising Subscriptions and Books	Daphne Matthews Marilyn Kopkin
Assistant	John Brooksbank

286

Useful Addresses

Craft Potters Association
William Blake House
7 Marshall Street
London W1V 1FD

Crafts Council
44a Pentonville Road
London N1 9BY

Welsh Arts Council
Holst House
9 Museum Place
Cardiff CF1 3NX

Scottish Arts Council
12 Manor Place
Edinburgh

Design Council
QED Centre
Main Avenue
Treforest Estate
Treforest CF37 5YR

Design Council
Business Design Centre
39 Corporation Street
Belfast BT1 3BA

Design Council
28 Haymarket
London SW1Y 4SU

Contemporary Applied Arts
43 Earlham Street
London WC2H 9LD

Ceramic Review
21 Carnaby Street
London W1V 1PH

Rural Development Commission
141 Castle Street
Salisbury
Wilts SP1 3TP

Scottish Design Council
45 Gordon Street
Glasgow G1 3RZ

Regional Arts Boards

Arts Board North West
12 Harter Street
Manchester M1 6HY

Eastern Arts
Cherry Hinton Hall
Cambridge CB1 4DW

East Midlands Arts
Mountfields House
Forest Road
Loughborough LE11 3HU

London Arts Board
Elme House
133 Long Acre
London WC2E 9AF

Northern Arts
10 Osborne Terrace
Newcastle-upon-Tyne NE2 1NZ

South East Arts
10 Mount Ephraim
Tunbridge Wells TN4 8AS

Southern Arts
13 Clement Street
Winchester SO23 3DQ

South West Arts
Bradninch Place
Gandy Street
Exeter EX4 3LS

West Midlands Arts
82 Granville Street
Birmingham B1 2LH

Yorkshire & Humberside Arts
21 Bond Street
Dewsbury WF13 1AX

CONTEMPORARY CERAMICS

CRAFT POTTERS
SHOP AND GALLERY

POTS   BOOKS   TOOLS   EXHIBITIONS

CONTEMPORARY
CERAMICS
7 MARSHALL STREET
LONDON . W1

OPEN MONDAY - SATURDAY 10-5.30pm THURSDAY 10-7pm

TELEPHONE 071-437 7605